D1328554

A *Primer* *on* FOOD, AGRICULTURE, *and* PUBLIC POLICY

A Primer o

The Primer series is under the editorial
supervision of PETER L. BERNSTEIN

FOOD, AGRICULTURE, and PUBLIC POLICY

~~~~~ Earl O. Heady

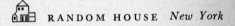 RANDOM HOUSE *New York*

Orel C. Heady *and* Jessie L. Heady

Preface

Food is not only essential for human life, it is the most pressing need of all goods and services for over half of the world's population. It represents the largest item in consumer expenditures, as much as 40 percent, even for developed countries in Western Europe.

In the United States, however, food has been an item of embarrassing abundance. We can produce so much of it and its real price is so low that few people suffer from lack of it. Our ability to produce food has provided the nation with one of its largest and most costly domestic problems: and we still have not solved the problem.

While the problem appears to be one of surplus production, it is much more than this. Attempts to solve it purely as a surplus problem never really get around to the real cause. In the first place, agriculture is highly productive because we have had national policies to make it so, and the stage and conditions of economic growth have promoted it. The rapid advance of agriculture has brought important gains to American society in the form of a low real price for food, release of resources to produce other goods and services of marginal urgency in an affluent society, and in providing a net annual transfer of around $20 billion invested in human resources. In contrast to some nations that use three-fourths of their labor resources in agriculture, American farming is so efficient that only 7 percent of our labor and capital is required to produce food. Not only do we have ample supplies for home use, we also export the product of one-fourth of our crop acres.

Still the advance of agriculture and these contributions to national society are accompanied by sacrifices to farm people. These sacrifices take the form of depressed incomes and low resource returns. They also take the forms of labor displaced from farming and of rural communities lacking positive opportunities in education and employment. The more basic policy question, then, is, How can agriculture continue these contributions to national progress and realize equitable returns in doing so?

In any case, the farm problem extends over the entire rural community. The advance of agriculture results in a smaller work force and population on farms. Hence, it has direct impact on the entire rural community and to nearly one-third of the nation's population living in nonmetropolitan areas. The farm problem is not likely to vanish until the corresponding problems of adjustment over the entire rural community are solved.

While half the world's population have inadequate diets today, the situation is likely to intensify. Current growth rates will double the world's population in thirty-five years, and in twenty-five years in some countries. It appears unrealistic that intelligent human beings could allow problems of food deficits and food surpluses to exist simultaneously. Yet problems of solving the pending world food crisis are more complex than just increasing United States output and shipping it abroad.

This book deals with the solution of food and farm problems in relation to those of the rural community, national economic growth, and international development; it analyzes the basic causes of farm problems, evaluates programs of the past, and outlines solutions for the long run. But it is for the student and citizen rather than the professional economist.

E.O.H.

Contents

PART I

PROBLEMS OF AGRICULTURE UNDER ECONOMIC GROWTH

CHAPTER 1

Food and Farm Problems

Food has always been a major concern of societies. From early times to the recent past, there was always too little of it in all countries. Without sufficient food, man is hungry and miserable. He cares little about the world around him, or its problems and opportunities either in economic development or social and political organization. The primary urge of man and society always has been to alleviate the three basic sources of misery: hunger, cold, and sickness.

Enough food to eliminate the misery of hunger is still a first concern over much of the world. In Asia, Africa, and South America the urgent want of the majority of people is still more food, enough to lessen the worry and misery of hunger, or to upgrade diets to extend the health and energy of the masses. While their populations are not on the verge of starvation, Russia and other Eastern European countries also have major problems in the tardy development of agriculture and an insufficient quantity and variety of food to match the more basic desires of their populations.

Thus at low stages of wealth and economic development, the basic drive of men and societies obviously revolves around agriculture. However, agriculture also is central to other aspects of ecónomic growth and the generation of wealth. Development of agriculture with improvement of the food supply is a necessary precondition for "takeoff" in the economic development of any nation. When agriculture is primitive and unproductive, nearly the whole of the work force must be engaged in farming, leaving very few people for work in industry and commerce. Even today, in some countries as much as 90 percent of the population is engaged in agriculture; adequate schools, housing, transportation, and consumer goods generally are not possible when only 10 percent is available for other pursuits. India, with 80 percent of its work force in agriculture, still faces extreme food shortages. The Soviet Union, at a more advanced stage of economic development, nevertheless requires around 40 percent of its work force to meet agricultural needs. In the United States, on the other hand, 53 percent of its population was engaged in food production at the farm level in 1840; 39 percent in 1900; and only about 6 percent in 1967, a figure that is expected to drop to 3 percent by 1980.

What does this mean? An American farm worker produced food for fewer than four persons in 1840. Today he produces enough for thirty-seven persons. It is little wonder, then, that the United States is able to produce a vastly greater per capita amount of housing, automobiles, home appliances, roads, schools, and other industrial goods and services than any other country in the world. Not only do we produce food in abundance and variety for the domestic population, but we also export the production from one out of every four crop acres, to supplement the food supply of the rest of the world.

But the abundance of food and the productivity of agri-

culture in the United States does not result purely from favorable resources and chance. Though the nation does have
some large areas with soils and climate particularly adapted
to crops such as corn or fruits and vegetables, some of our
most efficient food production is in locations where rainfall
is scant or soils do not have high natural productivity.

Food abundance has resulted largely because of the economic environment surrounding agriculture and the fact
that the nation has had some very specific public policies to
encourage agricultural development. While the United
States is not particularly noted for public planning, it has
had the world's best policies for developing agriculture and
increasing food output. Over a long period, the nation has
emphasized increasing the supply and lowering the prices of
resources and supporting the prices of farm products. It has
invested heavily in greater knowledge for farmers. It has developed effective machinery to get these policy instruments
into operation. The result is a large food supply and the
most productive agriculture in the world.

In fact, our problem has been the opposite of a food
shortage. For nearly forty years, the United States has been
plagued with food surpluses in one form or another. This is
a problem of wealthy societies; many nations would happily
trade places with us. Yet we have not been able to solve this
particular major peacetime economic problem as readily as
we have most other major national issues.

But to claim that the nation's mammoth farm dilemma is
one of food surpluses is to frame the problem too simply.
The basic problem is much more complex. It stems basically
from national economic growth and it must be solved accordingly. Solutions must extend beyond farming and into
the reaches of the entire rural community. Families in villages and towns over the countryside are caught up in these
problems of national economic growth as much as are those
on farms. No other countries have experienced this problem
in equal magnitude and intensity, either because they have

not attained the same level of economic development or because their agriculture is not dispersed over such a vast geographic area. Overly simple views of the farm problem as only one of temporary surpluses have led to major national disagreement and inappropriate policies in trying to reach solutions.

Directly, the farm problem does appear as one of too much production. Since the war, farm population has more than halved, and the work force in agriculture has declined by 40 percent. Yet the capacity of agriculture to produce food has grown constantly. We can produce 10 percent more food annually than required to meet domestic and commercial export needs at prices acceptable to the farm sector. And we can do so with one-eighth less land than needed a half-century ago.

Moreover, the producing capacity of agriculture will continue to expand and research suggests that, aside from breakthroughs in large foreign markets, our surplus potential will also grow during the next two decades. Despite a 50 percent growth in domestic food requirements and a doubling of exports, great capacity will still exist by 1980, even though the agricultural labor force is again halved and even more land can be freed from crop production for other urgent national uses.

The remarkable growth in our agricultural output and farm productivity is illustrated in the figures on the next page. Total farm output increased by 67 percent in twenty-five years while labor productivity in agriculture increased by 169 percent. Since the late 1950's, output per man hour in agriculture has gone up by 6.6 percent per year against 2.6 percent for non-farm industry.

We can apparently produce more with only a slight increase in total resources, while the amount of resources required to produce a unit of farm produce has declined remarkably. This very growth in efficiency brings two main problems to agriculture: (1) The rapid increase in output

YEAR	INDEX OF FARM OUTPUT	INDEX OF FARM LABOR PRODUCTIVITY	INDEX OF TOTAL RESOURCES USED	INDEX OF RESOURCES USED PER UNIT OF OUTPUT
1940	100	100	100	100
1945	116	126	102	88
1950	123	166	104	85
1955	138	180	105	77
1960	151	219	104	69
1965	167	269	104	62

results in lower prices and depresses incomes unless it is off-set by appropriate agricultural policy. (2) The leap in labor productivity means that we need fewer workers, many of whom not only must leave the industry where they are experienced but must move to new communities.

Agriculture is penalized by its rapid growth in producing ability because of the nature of the demand for food. The three major variables relating to food consumption are the price of food, the size of the population, and income per person. While more food is the urgent concern of people who have little, it has small value and little premium once a person has filled his stomach. Consequently, more food will be consumed only if prices decline very sharply, in an amount more than proportional to the increase in the quantity that people purchase and consume. A commodity with these characteristics has an *inelastic* demand in relation to price.

In contrast, the demand for many goods and services is *elastic* in relation to price. More output can be sold with a less than proportional decrease in price. An elastic demand for cars was the basis for Henry Ford's empire. In his maxim of success, he sized up the situation well: lower the price and increase the revenue by selling enough cars to more than make up for the reduction in the price per car.

Some examples can illustrate the difference between the

two situations. Thus, demand in Example A is elastic in relation to prices.

Example A. Elastic Demand with Price

ITEM	INITIAL	CHANGE	AFTER
Price	$1	− 10%	$.90
Quantity demanded	100	+ 20%	120
Revenue	$100	+ 8%	$108

Starting from an initial quantity of 100, price $1, and gross income of $100, a price decline of 10 percent results in a 20 percent increase in the quantity demanded. Demand is elastic: The percentage increase in the quantity sold is greater than the percentage decrease in price. Consequently, revenue increases because price does not decline by as great a percentage as output is increased. In contrast, under the inelastic demand of Example B, a 20 percent increase in output can be sold only if prices decline by

Example B. Inelastic Demand with Price

ITEM	INITIAL	CHANGE	AFTER
Price	$1	− 30%	$.70
Quantity demanded	100	+ 20%	120
Revenue	$100	− 16%	$84

30 percent. Demand is inelastic because quantity fails to rise as rapidly as price is reduced. The result is a decline in revenue.

We are talking about the elasticity or "stretch" in food consumption relative to its price. Stretch in relation to income, the example on page 9, refers to the income elasticity of demand. Both types of stretch or elasticity are important in farm income problems.

Unfortunately for agriculture in an advanced country, Example B parallels the demand situation. Demand with respect to price is inelastic: Since we can sell more only at a substantially lower price, incomes decline. To mention some representative commodities for the United States, a 1 percent increase in output will find a market only after the following declines in price: hogs—2.2 percent; wheat—2.5 percent; milk—2.4 percent; eggs—4.5 percent; potatoes—5 percent; feed grains—2.5 percent; and all food taken together—4.5 percent.*

The above figures refer to a given population and income. The demand for food obviously increases with a growth in population. Food output, therefore, can increase at about the same rate as the population without depressing prices and the income of farmers. However, since the growth in farm output has been at a greater rate than growth in population, the price elasticity figures cited above become effective. And without farm programs and foreign sales to offset this trend, the rapid growth in farm efficiency and food production threatens to reduce incomes for farmers.

But how about the third major variable affecting demand for food—per capita income? The per capita income effect on consumer expenditures varies depending on the commodity, the country, and the level of incomes. For poor populations with inadequate diets, food has a high demand elasticity with respect to income. The income elasticity indicates the percentage increase in expenditure for a 1 percent increase in per capita income. If people increase their expenditures on the commodity by more than 1 percent when their incomes rise by 1 percent, demand is elastic with respect to income. Obviously, an industry with a highly elastic

---

* However, while the demand for any one crop on the whole is highly inelastic, the demand for the product of any one individual farmer is infinitely or "perfectly" elastic. That is, he can sell as much as he can produce at the market price, but he can have no influence in raising the price. This fact catches him in the competitive squeeze explained in the next chapter.

demand in relation to income will be greatly favored by economic growth. In India, where per capita income is $60, a spurt in incomes would cause food demand to rise more rapidly than the mushrooming population. This situation even holds true in the United States for certain goods and services, such as recreation and health, where purchases "stretch" extremely as per capita incomes rise.

However, the income elasticity for food is only about one-tenth in the United States indicating a .1 percent increase in value of food purchases for each 1 percent increase in consumer income. While it varies among commodities, the income elasticity for the physical quantity of food is zero. For some foods the income elasticity is negative and the consumer eats less as his income rises. Outstanding examples are wheat and potatoes, where per capita consumption has declined by one-third since 1911; eggs and certain dairy products have declined by almost one-fourth since 1945. Gains in per capita incomes cause some increase in consumer expenditures for food, but most of the increase goes for packaging and services incorporated with food (such as frozen precooked foods or cake mixes). Some also goes for shifts in food quality. But the physical quantity of food does not increase for the affluent American who worries more about obesity than hunger. This low-income elasticity is another reason why farm prices and income tend to be depressed when farm output increases faster than population.

Obviously, a rapid increase in output is the wrong answer to the farmers' problem, even though many people offer this as a solution. Prices for farm products can be maintained only if the increase in output approximates the increase in domestic population and foreign demand. Over the period 1940-1965, however, growth in farm output was 67 percent while growth in United States population was only 48 percent.

While farmers are sometimes inclined to think that their difficulties arise from the plotting and collusion of the meat packers, flour millers, and other middlemen who "knock down" the consumer's dollar by over half before it gets back to the farm, this is untrue. The difference between the transaction at the grocery store and the farm gate is to be explained by America's level of affluence and the fact that the demand growth for services that go with food are much greater than for food itself. Neither government bureaucrats nor middlemen have created a vise to squeeze the farmer. The vise is provided by two hallmarks of economic development: on the one hand, by the farmer who produces so much; and on the other hand, by the consumer whose food demand is so inelastic.

The problem of farm surplus capacity first showed up in the 1920's when output started growing more rapidly than demand, became acute in the 1930's, and returned immediately in the 1950's after cessation of war-generated demand. The public, through governmental programs, took direct part in trying to solve the surplus and related income problems of agriculture as early as 1933. We have been so engaged ever since. Aside from shipment of surplus food as foreign aid, the policies in effect over the past fifteen years, under both Republican and Democratic administrations, are variations of those initiated in 1933. They center on payments to persuade farmers to divert land from surplus crops, price supports and loans to farmers for withholding crops from the market, government acquisition of stocks that are similarly held from the market, food stamp plans or distribution of surplus commodities to needy families to stimulate consumption, and related programs. The public investment in programs to control or reduce production, raise prices, and otherwise augment farm income has totaled over $60 billion since 1933, more than half of which we laid out in the last fifteen years.

Even with these investments and persistent efforts, we have not come to a long-run solution of the nation's basic farm problems. Left to the market alone, with complete elimination of public programs and outlays, output would erupt,* prices would be greatly depressed, and many farmers would go bankrupt in the short run. But if we continue the same set of programs another fifteen years at current expenditure rates, the nation will lay out another $75 billion, only to have some of the same problems with us in about the same form as today.

Thus, even with our large farm programs, the income level of farm workers is still far below the national average. Disposable income per person in agriculture was only $1,270 in 1964, as compared to $2,317 per person in all other industries. While economic equality does not require the same dollar income in agricultural and urban centers, the difference is great enough to be striking. And the absolute difference in income per capita has grown over time. The difference, only $430 in 1940, was $1,035 in 1966. In 1964, the year of most recent data, the median earnings of skilled workmen in the United States was $6,013. In contrast, median earnings were only $2,247 for farmers and $1,163 for farm laborers.

Farming is not, of course, a homogeneous industry. The figures cited above are averages. While farming is generally a small business, there is great variation in sizes and incomes of farms. Agriculture has a disproportionate share of the nation's poor families. Recent data show agriculture to have 16 percent of all American families with incomes under $3,000, the breaking point used to define poverty in establishing the Office of Economic Opportunity. In contrast, agriculture has only 6 percent of the nation's families. Or expressed in another way, most recent figures showed 43 percent of farm families to have incomes under $3,000, with

---

* It might seem paradoxical that output would erupt when all farmers know that prices would decline by an even greater proportion. The answer to this paradox is in the intensely competitive character of farming and is discussed at length in the next chapter.

only 12 percent of nonfarm families falling in this category. Obviously, then, agriculture not only is faced with surpluses and relative depression of income, but it also contains a concentration of the nation's poverty problem. If we add in all rural families, 46 percent of the nation's families with income under $3,000 reside in rural areas. Of course, a large number of older retired persons reside on farms in rural communities where $3,000 will buy a fair living.

We include all rural persons in the low-income figures above because nonfarm families in rural communities are caught up in the same general problem that farmers have to face. Low income to farmers has its second-round effects in reduced sales of local merchants, who then realize lower incomes. The exodus of farm people from rural areas similarly reduces local retail volume. Lower incomes, the selective effect of migration in leaving older persons to dominate the population, reduced capital values of local businesses, and a reduced tax base also have an important impact on the services and facilities of the rural community. These forces make fewer tax funds available for the support of schools, recreation, and other facilities that are accepted and more abundant in urban areas. Rural schools already have lower quality education and limited capability in training youth for today's occupational opportunities than do city schools. Thus national society suffers as farm youth are fed into the labor force with technical training and education that limits their productivity. This is an ironic fate for that sector of the economy which has led the way toward higher efficiency and productivity.

Society also loses because a large number of full-time farmers are on low-production farms. They are not needed to produce the nation's food supply and produce only a dribble of it now. Not only is their labor unproductive in agriculture but it also contributes little to the nation's economy. Moreover, many persons in the small towns of farm communities are similarly unproductive and have little opportunity to participate in the nation's progress. The lot of both groups should be a major concern for society.

Obviously the farm problem is more than a simple one of farm surpluses and low prices. It is part of an even broader problem. Low earnings to labor in agriculture prevail over the entire world, shown in the list below based on the most recent data available for a sample of countries. The right hand column indicates the labor income in agriculture of each country as a percentage of labor income in nonfarm industries in that same country.

Austria	40	India	42
Belgium	63	Italy	51
Brazil	34	Mexico	18
Canada	63	Norway	50
Chile	46	Pakistan	47
Egypt	36	Portugal	43
France	38	Sweden	58
Finland	42	Turkey	16
Germany	44	United States	60
Hungary	56	USSR	26

Thus income per worker in agriculture is only 44 percent of income for nonfarm workers in Germany, 60 percent in the United States, 42 percent in India, and 26 percent in Russia. In two-thirds of the cases shown, labor income in agriculture is less than one-half that of nonfarm workers.

To understand the real foundation of farm problems, we must look far and deep. This is obvious from the figures above. In later chapters we will see just how widespread is the phenomenon of low returns to human resources in agriculture.

Certain beliefs about farms and farmers are widespread. At one extreme, many people believe that farmers are poor peasants, that farming is a simple way of life, and that only

dull persons remain in the countryside to produce the nation's food supply. Commercial farm families in the United
States, those producing most of the marketings and who are
in business for purposes other than subsistence or to provide
a retirement activity, or who are not simply stranded there,
are not poor. They own automobiles, televisions, and other
modern home appliances. They have a standard of living
excelling that of city populations in most other countries.
The farm operator works long days over most of the years,
but the cultural orientation of himself and his family is
largely the same as the middle-class urban family. Adding
together the poor, the rich, and others, farm families are
wealthier than nonfarm families. As shown in the figures
below, farm families averaged together have a net worth
twice as great as that of nonfarm families. These figures
refer to assets of families, not of corporations except as they
are represented by securities owned by families.

TYPE OF ASSET	ALL UNITED STATES FAMILIES	FARM FAMILIES
Home	$5,975	$5,501
Auto	637	681
Business	3,913	25,767
Insurance, etc.	1,376	1,278
Cash, securities, etc.	11,170	11,233
Personal debt	483	486
Average net worth	22,588	43,973
Median net worth	7,550	26,250

Of course, farming in total is a big industry. Its assets,
around $250 billion, are equal to two-thirds the value of
current assets of all United States corporations, or one-half
the value of all stocks listed on the New York Stock Exchange.
Commercial farmers must apply broad intellect to their operations. Farm businesses are complex; the skill required of
farmers exceeds greatly that for many laboring, supervisory,

and management jobs in major industries. Because he deals with so many machines, animals, and plants, the commercial farmer must be a good engineer, biologist, and chemist. Yet his salary as an applied specialist in these fields is much less than that of his counterparts elsewhere.

At the other extreme, some city dwellers hold an image of the farmer as a "country slicker" who drives a Cadillac and lives luxuriously on handouts represented by public subsidies. A few large-scale commercial farmers do receive big government payments, although representing a small portion of their income, as part of the subsidy scheme to "solve the farm problem." However, the typical commercial farmer receives only a few hundred dollars in government subsidies.

As the figures for 1964 show—aside from the largest farmers, the top 10.7 percent, who get a whopping 55 percent of all payments—the amount of government payments per farm

SIZE OF FARM IN SALES	NUMBER OF FARMS IN THOUSANDS	PER- CENTAGE OF FARMS	GOVERN- MENT PAYMENTS PER FARM	PERCENTAGE OF INCOME FROM GOVERNMENT
$20,000 or more	384	10.7	$2,391	18.5
10,000-19,999	594	16.6	670	8.8
5,000-9,999	609	17.0	350	6.4
2,500-4,999	463	13.0	173	3.9
Less than $2,500	1,523	42.6	51	1.2
All farms	3,573	100.0	472	8.8

is not large. Nearly 90 percent of all farmers have government payments averaging $650 or less and nearly three-fourths have average payments of $350 or less. The 55.6 percent of all farmers with lowest incomes average $173 or less in government payments. This 55.6 percent of farmers also averages only 1.8 percent of its income from government payments. Two things are obvious from these data: (1) the great majority of farmers are not getting rich directly from public payments; (2) government programs are doing very little for low-income farm families.

Another myth, sometimes popularized by editorials in leading national publications, presents the farmer as the most regimented of United States businessmen, a lackey of government bureaucrats who tell him how much to plant and when to sell. But he is hardly this. Farmers are much less regimented than laborers in industry, supervisory and management personnel in the typical large business, school-teachers, and other public employees. Perhaps the freedom of being their own boss keeps many people in farming when they could make more elsewhere.

Indeed, government programs have been largely voluntary. Controls or restraints on production have never been very severe, perhaps explaining why supply-reduction programs have not always been very successful. Regimentation has not grown and controls on production are probably less restraining now than in the 1930's. Only about 25 percent of farm marketings are represented by controlled crops, thus emphasizing the cost of programs for farm commodity sectors that depend most on government programs.

There is a myth that family farms will disappear. At each election, politicians pose the "scare" that large corporations are "just around the corner" and will certainly liquidate the nation's typical family farm structure. It is true, economic development, which has lowered the price of capital and caused it to be substituted for labor, has given rise to some important scale economies in agriculture. Larger farms are required to spread the fixed costs and give efficient use of modern machines and equipment. Sandwiched with this development has been the creation of large factory-type farms, found mostly in large cattle-feeding operations of the West and mammoth poultry units in the East and South. Mainly, however, once a farm size is expanded to allow efficient use of a modern set of machines, there is small advantage to larger units that simply duplicate the equipment. A farm family can usually handle a modern set of machinery and realize its main scale economies. Consequently, the size of family farms is increasing but the family farm is not declining in importance. The future simply will be one of fewer but larger family farms as the dominant structure of agriculture. The proportion of hired nonfamily labor has actually declined in the last twenty years. As a matter of fact, one problem is to have a greater proportion of adequate-sized family farms.

Farming is still largely a family business; each farm uses an average of only 1.75 man years of labor. There are, of course, a few highly specialized units, such as fruit and vegetable farms, which use a large crew of hired labor. But only 6 percent of all farms hire more than a year and one-half of labor. Excluding these, the typical farm uses only a year and one-half of labor in total. More than three-fourths of this is family labor, including the farmer or operator and his wife and children. The majority of farms use nothing but family labor, except for a few days of help during harvesting time; the farmer, often aided by his wife and children, serves as manager as well as laborer.

Furthermore, the capital comes from savings by the family or borrowed funds based on these accumulations. Hence, the liability from losses by low prices or poor crops also falls entirely on the family. Farms do not obtain capital through the sale of common stock with limited liability, as do large-scale corporations. While the amount varies with the location and crops produced, the typical commercial farmer manages a total capital investment of about $90,000. This amount appears small for a business against that of large corporations, but it represents about $50,000 per typical commercial farm worker. This ratio of capital per worker is much greater than the average of industries.

While farms in all parts of the country differ greatly from one another, it is true that the larger ones, which are still small compared to business corporations, dominate sales. About 30 percent of farms have yearly gross sales of more than $10,000; one-sixth have sales between $5,000 and $10,000; and more than one-half have sales under $5,000. Farming expenses, about 70 percent of gross income, must be subtracted from these amounts, the remainder being net income. The 30 percent with sales of more than $10,000, (around 1 million farms) market 81 percent of the nation's agricultural product. Even more startling, about 45 percent of farms have sales over $5,000 but market 92 percent of the total. The 70 percent with sales of less than $10,000, 2.5 million farms, market only 21 percent of the total product, and the 55 percent with sales of less than $5,000 market only 8 percent.

The squeeze from rapid technical advance and commercialization of agriculture falls especially on the small farm. Few of the nearly 2 million with sales of $5,000 or less have a favorable economic outlook in farming. The modest government subsidies they receive cannot lift their incomes to an adequate level in today's standards. Most of them must eventually disappear. These farms are too small to use modern technology efficiently, and they cannot provide full employment to the operator, let alone compete with larger farms. Agriculture has made mammoth adjustments in the number and size of farms and in the labor force over the last two decades, but it still has a long way to go.

Even the largest one-fourth of the farms with sales of $10,000 and over are still small businesses. They average about 300 acres of cropland and have productive assets valued at about $125,000. If we exclude retirement and part-time units, farms with sales under $10,000 average about 73 acres and have $32,000 in assets. (Farms with sales between $5,000 and $10,000 represent nearly one-half of the latter group and average 143 acres of cropland and about $47,000 in capital.) At the last count, farms with sales over $10,000 had net farm incomes of around $8,000, while those with less than $10,000 in sales averaged $2,600 in income from farm sources.

Families on small units are increasingly turning toward off-farm work. Around one-fourth of all farms are part-time units, with one or more family members working in other occupations. Over 35 percent of the income for the farm population comes from nonfarm sources. One-half million farms serve mainly as places of retirement for older persons. Some detail on the net income of these various groups is provided below.

SIZE OF FARM IN SALES	AVERAGE FAMILY INCOME FROM FARMING	FROM OFF-FARM	TOTAL
$10,000 or more	$7,982	$1,978	$9,960
$5,000-9,999	3,451	1,567	5,018
Less than $5,000			
Mainly farming	1,938	1,517	3,455
Part-time and retirement	579	3,521	4,100

All these groups have considerably higher incomes than families in most nations of the world. It would appear that they should have a good country living. We must remember, however, that the farm portion of these incomes comes, on the average for all farms, from about one and one-half workers and $70,000 in capital. The incomes from farming are small, relative to the amount of resources used to produce them. If the average American farmer were to deduct a 5 percent return on his capital, he would have realized a return of 50¢ per hour or less on the labor of himself and his family. Or if he had charged for the family labor used, even at the low level of farm wage rates, he would have had a return of only about 2.5 percent on his capital in recent years. Here lies an obvious reason for the rapid migration of young people from farms and the turn toward nonfarm employment to supplement income from farming.

The public has pumped a considerable sum of money into agriculture through various farm programs. For the majority of farmers, however, these programs had the main effect of stabilizing incomes, or keeping them from falling lower in the postwar period. After the decline following the end of the war, net income to the farming industry finally was stabilized at around $12.5 billion. Recent inflationary trends and price improvement from programs have boosted it somewhat, but even so, with income per capita at a low level, the main hope for income improvement for many farm families is through fewer farms and fewer people in agriculture.

We can sort United States farms into several convenient groups. Of the 3.5 million units, around 1.3 million are homes of part-time workers, retired persons, and other special groups, all of whom produce less than 4 percent of the nation's farm sales. They are already a step away from agriculture and in a few years most will be retired or concerned mainly about factory wages and working conditions. They realize little benefit from government farm programs since they are outside agriculture in an occupational or professional sense. Although they are not really part of the long-run commercial farm problem, they are part of the rural community problem.

Some 665,000 units are full-time farms with sales of less than $5,000 and deriving the majority of their income from farming. While they constitute 19 percent of all farms, they market less than 6 percent of the nation's total farm product. They are truly the low-income units of agriculture.

Forty-five percent of farms, a total of 1.6 million, have sales over $5,000—these farms produce 92 percent of the market product, and are the core of the farming business. They are also the core of the basic farm problem. It is to them that government has mainly directed its farm programs. A large share of these, except those run by people near retirement, will remain in agriculture and probably have the best hopes in the future by doing so. However, not even this number may be able, or should be encouraged, to remain in the occupation. We are certainly headed toward a time when considerably fewer commercial farms will continue to exist. But the downward adjustment will provide some rough going for many farm families, particularly those who must liquidate and leave. Their first attempt will continue to be that of improving their position in agriculture by adopting new technology and expanding their output. But this is not easy. It invokes the inelasticity of demand, so that consumers gain in lower food prices and farmers sacrifice in lower income. It can be accomplished by some, only if others give up farming.

CHAPTER II

The Role of Agriculture in Economic Progress

The inability of agriculture to retain an equitable share of its contribution to economic progress stems from the nature of the farm business, the structure of the agricultural industry, and the role of agriculture in economic growth. Improvement of agriculture is necessary at low stages of development before economic takeoff for a nation is possible. At this stage of development, agriculture also may gain in income about in proportion to its contribution to the national economy. However, at advanced stages of economic development, as per capita incomes rise to high levels and consumers are well fed, further rapid advances of agriculture can cause income problems to fall on the farmer.

This is true even though agriculture continues to make a net contribution to national economic growth through reductions in the real cost of food and in providing the human capital that moves with youth to the nonfarm labor force.

The net migration of people from farms, taking with them the costs of rearing and education, has averaged over a million persons per year since 1940. Some estimates suggest that this flow of capital, a one-way net transfer from the farm community, amounts to over $20 billion annually in the United States.

Society realizes gains with further improvement of agriculture, but they bring with them problems of how those gains should be distributed and who should bear the costs.

Though the nature of the farm business itself leads to progress, it also provides an ineffective means for retaining its contributions to national progress. Each farm is a small business firm, and though the number of farms has halved since it reached a peak of about 6.5 million in 1920, there are still so many of these small businesses that they are extremely competitive. In fact, agriculture is the only major industry of pure competition in our economy. Without organization, the farmer serves as a "price taker," a distinguishing characteristic of pure competition. While he can sell any amount available at the market price, he must accept the price given back to him in the market. He cannot set a price for his individual products, as in autos or computers, and then adjust the amount of sales accordingly.

Thus the competitive conditions of farming differ greatly from other major industries; business firms need not, and seldom do, serve directly as price takers. Though market competition exists, it differs greatly from the pure competition of agriculture. For example, in contrast to agriculture, where the number is large but the size is small, the automobile industry has very few firms but each is very large. In fact, the sales of a single American automobile firm exceed the gross national product of many individual countries. Under these conditions, one firm's actions has an immediate impact on other firms in the industry. Consequently, the manufacturer decides on a price, then quotes it. He can differentiate his product from that of other firms, through style and advertising. If he decides that a higher price and a lower sales volume will bring him more profit than lower price and greater volume, he can act accordingly. But an individual farmer controls too small a share of marketings to have any impact on price. If he charges a price higher than the market price, buyers will not take his product. They will buy it at a lower price from other farmers who produce the same product.

In the case of automobiles and other such industries, short-run competition is usually through appeals other than price alone. The structure of these industries provides some short-run means for retaining a share of the gains from improvement and contributions to progress. Over the long run, of course, competition prevails not only among car manufacturers but also with other types of transportation. Yet it stands that these firms are not price takers. They may follow the price set by one producer or the price may simply stabilize at a convenient level because of the small number.

In the case of individual laborers, though they were once price takers, few now are; instead, unions provide them with market or bargaining power. Of course, individuals compete for a given job, even though the wage or salary level is determined, and labor of a particular skill and occupation competes with that of other fields, or even with capital in the form of machines and automation. But still, labor typically bargains as a group rather than as individual workers. Through this countervailing market power, it can deal effectively with the firms of a particular industry to establish wage levels and obtain a share of the gains from increased labor productivity.

Not only is the farmer's competitive position weak, but the fact that agriculture depends on climate also gives rise to great instability of prices. Prices fluctuate violently between years of good and bad harvests because the total demand for farm output is so inelastic. Prices are high in years of low yields, but farmers have little to sell. In years when their volume is large they get little for it because prices fall sharply. Even from season to season, there typically is a wide spread between prices at harvest and other times of the year.

The many small producers respond to price in a manner that gives rise to cycles in production. In years when prices are high, they make plans to produce more hogs next year. Since it takes a year from planning to marketing, price has declined drastically by the time increased output from thousands of farms reaches the market. Penalized in income under the low prices, the individual then decides to produce less in the next period. But so do his neighbors, and when their smaller product hits the market the price is again high. So goes the cycle for hogs and various other products.

In contrast, the prices for inputs used in farm production do not follow similar short-run cycles and variability. Consequently, net farm income fluctuates even more widely than farm product prices.

Under the highly inelastic demand for food (Example B in Chapter I), farmers can indeed increase their incomes if they cut back on production: demand remaining the same, prices will rise sharply. But the competitive nature of agriculture prevents the individual farmer from improving his position in this way. Even if he reduces output by 50 percent, his effect on the total amount marketed is too small to cause prices to change and will only sacrifice income because he will sell less at the same price. Nor would other farmers gain from his action because the market effect is too weak to raise prices.

Because of the competitive structure of agriculture, individual farmers attempt to improve their position by turning their efforts in the opposite direction; namely, by taking price as given and increasing output. By selling more at the same price, if costs are not increased too much, they expect to increase profits. Yet when all farmers together use this strategy, the growth in output and impact in the market is great. Because of the inelastic demand for total farm output, prices decline by a greater proportion than the increase in output. The mass effect is a decline in income for both the industry and individual farmers.

These circumstances squeeze the individual farmer. New technology that increases output and replaces farm labor pours continuously into agriculture from two sources: (1) the public, which invests heavily in improved farm technical processes, and (2) industry, which is in a continuous search for new methods involving capital materials to sell to farmers. The single farmer may well know that if all farmers, acting individually, try to beat the price taker situation by using new technology and increasing output, the mass result will be proportionately lower prices and reduced incomes. Yet he cannot sit back and maintain his income position by holding output constant while others improve technology and increase output. If he does, he will sell the same amount at a lower price. Again his profit will be reduced. He will be better off if he also adopts the new technology and sells more at the lower price, rather than sell the same amount at the lower price. While his income is reduced in both cases, the reduction is less using this strategy than in simply maintaining his output.

The competitive nature of agriculture thus forces farmers to increase resource productivity and extend output. They continuously search for new ways to increase yields. In short, in the absence of offsetting government programs, the rapid advance of agriculture depresses prices extremely and lowers net income of farmers in aggregate.

To keep their income apace with national trends, or even to maintain their income, many persons are forced to turn to other occupations. Some farmers who try to retain their income position by extending volume of output buy land and enlarge their units. Hence, there is room for fewer farms. This squeeze means, of course, that the nation's food can be produced with fewer resources: The work force of agriculture has been reduced by 7 million workers in the last three decades. And we can produce twice as much food with 60 million fewer acres of cropland than in 1925.

These changes, which cause income and other problems to fall on agriculture, provide direct benefits to consumers. Along with the decline in the real price for food, farm workers are freed to produce more cars, schools, roads, television sets, personal services, and other commodities to which affluent consumers attach greater urgency. Land can be diverted to recreational use, roads, airports, and forests—uses that have higher priority for high-income urban families. Our large population has not, as some feared, encountered a scarcity of land for these purposes. The step-up in agricultural efficiency greatly increases the amount of land that can be so diverted, and national economic growth is generally promoted as the nation's expanding food supply is produced with less labor and land.

The proportion of the consumer's expenditure that goes for food has declined steadily from this process and is now less than half what it was fifteen years ago (if we consider the same basket of food over the two periods). While the average American family uses only 18.5 percent of its disposable income for food purchases, the Soviet family must use over 50 percent for food that is in a fairly raw state without the embellishments of the American supermarket. The figure is around 40 percent for Western Europe and Japan and as high as 70 percent for much of Asia, Africa, and South America.

Only about 7 percent of the consumer's total expenditures actually go for food as represented by the product of the farmer. Nowhere else in the world, or even in the dreams of man, has food come so close to being a free good such as air and water. The United States is the only country where the typical family spends more per year on automobiles or recreation than on food.

Prices of food at the grocery store may seem to reflect little or none of these gains in United States farming efficiency. Yet the attainments through technological improvement of agriculture are very real, as illustrated by the data below indicating the amount of food purchased with an hour's work by an American factory worker.

ITEM		1929	1939	1963
Potatoes	(lb.)	17.0	25.1	37.8
Butter	(lb.)	1.0	1.9	3.3
Eggs	(doz.)	1.1	2.0	3.6
Milk	(pint)	7.8	10.2	19.0
Bread	(loaves)	6.4	7.9	11.4
Bacon	(lb.)	1.3	2.0	3.6
Steak	(lb.)	1.2	1.7	2.3

As we can see from the table, since 1929 food has declined in real price so much that the amount purchased with an hour of labor has approximately tripled. From 1948 to 1965, the average expenditure of urban families for food increased by 17 percent, from $940 to $1,100. However, the farm value of the food—boxes, packaging, etc., omitted—actually decreased 14 percent, from $466 to $401.

Less than half of what the consumer spends at the grocery is for food from the farmer. The major proportion of what he pays goes for the packaging, ready-mixing, freezing, slicing, and other time-saving characteristics that American families and housewives desire as they become richer. In fact, only 38¢ of the consumer's dollar is for the farmer's product. Grocery stores are engaged more in selling the convenience and services that go with food than in selling food produced by the farmer. There is nothing wrong with this trend; it only obscures the consumer's knowledge of his gain from increased farming efficiency. If affluent American consumers could not buy these services with food at the supermarket, they would simply pay a lower price for the grocery store items. Then they would use the savings at the grocery store to buy the same services elsewhere, perhaps by taking unsliced loaves to a specialized bread-slicing shop, by hiring a maid to mix the cake—and by buying their Cokes, beer, and nylon stockings at other stores.

Since farmers contribute immensely to consumer and national welfare, and make sacrifices in doing so, why don't they band together and acquire the market or bargaining power of labor unions or the small number of firms that make up other industries? Farmers have made some sizable attempts to join together voluntarily and reduce output. They did so in early days for tobacco and in the late 1920's for other major commodities. These attempts met with little success; control over the output of individuals was ineffective and the voluntary programs were unsuccessful.

Though today there are associations of producers for almost every farm commodity, typically the number in each group is still so large that voluntary control on output and prices is again ineffective. One farmer sits with a group and agrees on the merits of restrained output to raise prices, but he goes home and increases his output, expecting the others to follow the conventional wisdom and to gain from the price rise as they reduce output. Add up the actions of all individual farmers who do this and the plan is defeated.

This is why farmers have had to turn to federal legislation either to provide legal restraints on output or to provide the machinery for control. Federal legislation has provided marketing orders and agreements that allow farmers to vote quotas and output restraints on themselves. These agreements, which are binding on the individual and cause him to reduce output as a means of improving prices, but which must be voted into effect by farmers, have been used for only a few products such as fruit, vegetables, and milk. Mostly, however, production control has come through the government's paying farmers to leave their land idle.

Furthermore, the small scale of business restrains the farmer from developing new research and product improvements that only he can use. Hence, farmers have turned to the public, through both state and federal governments, to provide these services and information. Research and new technical knowledge is thus provided by the public through a network of sixty-eight state agricultural colleges and the many research facilities of the U.S. Department of Agriculture. But since these are public institutions, the new technology and knowledge that they generate is also public property and is fed freely and rapidly to all farmers. An individual farm cannot, as is common practice in industry, keep new technical knowledge secret and release it only in the form of its own product under the schedule that it chooses.

The family nature of farming also presents a special circumstance leading to inflexible supplies and depressed incomes. Since the resources used are those of the family and are mostly geared to farming, reduced prices and income do not cause a reduction in output as readily as in industry. As prices decline and incomes are depressed, the family simply continues the same inputs and takes a lower return on its resources for the time being. In contrast, the business firm or manufacturer tends to hold the price line and let the volume of sales fall off. For example, the price of steel and automobiles either has been stationary or rising in every postwar year. Yet sales of these two commodities sometimes declined by over 25 percent. In contrast, over most of the same period, the general trend was for more output and lower prices in agriculture.

The farm family is tied culturally and geographically to its occupation. This is another reason that it remains on the farm, producing more at a lower price even though incomes are depressed. Older farm couples have few skills that they can move successfully to another location and occupation. It is also hard for them to adapt from country to city living.

The picture is quite different for the industrial worker, who may change occupations while remaining in the same community and house. He simply drives a different direction to another firm or plant in the same city. Even if he moves to another city, the cultural shock is less than for the farm family moving from open country to a medium-sized town. These conditions that restrain labor mobility, causing it to be slower than technological progress and tardy relative to birth rates in agriculture, explain why farm labor over the entire world has lower income than nonfarm labor.

We have looked at the unique structure of agriculture and individual farms that leads to consumer benefits and, at the same time, to the specific problems of the industry. We also may ask whether these problems of farm size and structure always penalized agriculture to the same degree. We shall see that in each of three stages of economic growth— the traditional or pre-takeoff stage, the takeoff or rapidly developing stage, and the mature or advanced-growth stage —agriculture realizes gains of different degrees and types.

Technical advance of agriculture is basic to the economic development of nations. Many new nations are now struggling to advance farming so that they can push ahead more rapidly in industrialization. In the pre-takeoff stage, the contribution of agriculture to society is largely biological. Sufficient food must be available to prevent malnutrition and to provide for physical activity of workers.

In this stage, the majority of the population must work on farms to produce food for its own subsistence. Labor is not free to concentrate on industry and public services, since people are fully engaged in producing enough to eat just for themselves. They are outside of the commercial market. Since they sell little or nothing, national developments have little impact on them; nor do price rises or declines. In any given year, the weather and natural forces are more nearly the determinant of their welfare. Not until they move out of this stage can significant economic growth take place.

Starting from such inadequate food supplies and the undeveloped agricultures that are their cause, national economic growth that materially raises per capita income will also increase the prosperity of agriculture. In countries having ill-fed and poor populations, food has a high demand elasticity with respect to income—that is, the demand for food will rise faster than incomes as people strive to improve their diets from near-starvation levels. In underdeveloped countries, the income elasticity of demand for some food may be greater than one, particularly for many of the nutritionally desirable and high quality foods. With this elasticity, a 10 percent increase in per capita income could be expected to increase expenditures on food by more than 10 percent. Earnings of resources and family incomes in agriculture will rise and even more resources will be drawn into farming.

Expanding demand and high income elasticity could cause the growth in food output to benefit both consumers and farmers. Even with somewhat lower prices, the great expansion in the sales of farm production under conditions of highly elastic demand could increase farm income. At the same time, consumers could gain in lower real prices for food. Under these conditions, increased farm output results in what can be called *positive-sum* welfare outcome for the major groups concerned. The result to farmers is positive, because their incomes increase. The result to consumers is positive, because they can either buy more food and a higher quality diet with the same expenditures, or they can buy the same quality and quantity with a smaller outlay. If the outcomes are added for the two groups, the benefits have to be positive: The sum of two positives, regardless of their size, is always positive.

While the contribution of agriculture is highly biological in the first or pre-takeoff stage of development, it becomes highly economic in the takeoff or rapidly developing stage. The major function of agriculture in economic growth now involves a step-up in efficiency to allow the release of labor from farming. Not all persons can be employed in producing their own food.

However, the release of labor from farming is possible only when national economic development is rapid and industry needs labor. As farming is improved and labor productivity is increased, an increasing proportion of the labor force can then move to industry to allow growth in directions other than farming.

For American agriculture, this positive-sum situation existed from 1820 to 1920. With favorable demand conditions, agriculture and its output grew rapidly. The farm population and the agricultural labor force quadrupled during this period. Because of the high farm birth rate, some migration from farms could take place and the remaining work force was able to provide food for a national population that increased seven-fold in the same period. A rapidly increasing population and growing per capita income, plus expansion in world outlets, provided a very favorable demand situation. For the primitive technology of the time and aside from temporary setbacks, agriculture had a growing prosperity, especially as consumers greatly upgraded their diets with improvements in income.

While gaining greatly from this growth elsewhere in the economy, agriculture contributed substantially to it. It did so as some children, born and reared on the farm with the costs paid accordingly, moved to industry. Labor resources, with a good-sized investment in their education and training, were supplied by the farm sector at no cost to the industrial sector. Furthermore, the surplus capital accumulated in the farm sector was largely transferred to the nonfarm sector, providing a means for industrial expansion greater than possible from the capital generated within it. Capital flowed as inheritances with those who migrated from farms and as the main source of taxes to provide the overhead capital going into schools, roads, and other public facilities.

The mature stage of economic growth in the relation of agriculture to national development was attained around 1920. The level of per capita incomes, while much lower than at the present and still increasing, was now high enough that growth in per capita food consumption slowed almost to a standstill. Agriculture then ceased to be the "growth industry" it has been up to this time. It could no longer expand and draw labor into it. If it were not to be penalized in income, it could no longer expand output more rapidly than the growth in population and fluctuations in foreign markets permitted. The basic woes of American agriculture had begun.

Agriculture in wealthy, growing economies where rapid improvements in farm technology take place, generally will be faced with a cost-price squeeze and a less favorable income situation than in other major economic sectors. The reason lies partly in the magnitudes of income elasticities of demand. Industries that produce commodities with high income elasticities of demand are in the most advantageous position to use more resources and increase output as national and per capita income grow. They also pay premium incomes to the resources used in them. Those industries of low income elasticities, such as agriculture, are much less favored, largely because they represent commodities for which the consumer is well supplied and has little capacity for further expansion.

As consumer income increases, food no longer is his major concern. There is a limit to the size of the consumer's stomach, but he can stretch greatly the quantity of services he uses with food and the amount of nonfood consumed. He wants relatively more home appliances, better housing, medicine and health services, recreation, travel, and education. He does not buy any more pounds of food, but largely changes the composition from fats, starchy foods, and such staples to more fresh vegetables, better cuts of meat, fruits, etc. The number of pounds of food consumed per person in the United States has not increased in the last fifty years. Per capita consumption of food energy now is 10 percent less than in 1910, the parallel decline being 24 percent for carbohydrates and 6 percent for proteins. "Good living" no longer means simply getting enough food, clothing, and shelter for subsistence.

Under further economic growth, use of national resources shifts accordingly. The proportion of national income from agriculture declines and a smaller proportion of labor and other resources are needed in it. This tendency is illustrated in the table below, which shows the percentage of national

COUNTRY	1870	1960
Canada	43%	7%
Denmark	45	18
France	49	12
Germany	24	8
Italy	56	18
Sweden	40	5
United States	36	4

income coming from agriculture at two points in time for several highly developed countries. In all the countries listed, agricultural income as a proportion of national income has declined drastically.

These aspects of growth would not alone cause the problem of low resource returns in agriculture. For example, with a growth in farm output at a *slower* rate than population growth, and with the income elasticity of demand for food lower than 1 (Example B, Chapter I), farming would still be a profitable industry. The retarded rate of growth in food supply relative to population and demand expansion would provide highly favorable terms of trade for the agricultural industry. While agriculture would still decline in the share of national income and national resources represented by the industry, earnings of resources employed and family incomes would move sharply upward. In the United States, however, the output of food has increased *more rapidly* than the growth in consumer demand, with two effects: (1) the share of agriculture in the national economy has declined even more rapidly; (2) farm incomes and resource earnings have been highly depressed as compared to those of other economic sectors.

But even in the absence of rates of technical improvement that are more rapid than growth in demand for food, and aside from the magnitude of income elasticities of demand, economic growth causes the share of agriculture in the national economy to decline because growth both invites and brings about changes in the resource mix used by agriculture itself. Without this effect, agriculture would decline in the proportion of national resources employed and income produced, but it would still use more resources in an absolute sense. Agriculture's decline in relation to the rest of the economy would by itself only parallel income elasticities of demand that are lower in agriculture than in other industrial and service sectors. However, the very large decline in the proportion of labor used by agriculture in advanced countries as illustrated in the table on page 38, indicates tremendous and persistent technological advance in agricultural production. For example, Canadian agriculture used 50 percent of the nation's labor force in 1870, but only 10 percent in 1960. Agriculture, which employed 38 percent of the United States labor force in 1870, in 1960 employed only 8 percent.

Consumers express their wishes through prices paid in the

COUNTRY	1870	1930	1960
Belgium	37%	22%	7%
Canada	50	31	10
Denmark	45	19	18
France	75	36	23
Germany	42	17	14
Italy	62	47	30
Sweden	68	39	11
United States	38	22	8

market. As incomes increase, they are unwilling to place premium prices on farm products, saying that they do not need more food except as there are more persons to feed. Hence, American demand for food grows at about the rate of population growth. In contrast, as incomes grow, consumers are willing to pay increasingly high prices for nonfarm products. But in bidding higher prices for nonfarm goods and services, the consumer also bids or keeps up the cost of steel, labor, petroleum, and other materials that produce luxury goods. Consequently, the cost of tractors, lumber, fuel, fertilizer, and other cost items of the farm is kept up.

This, then, is one major cause of the farm price squeeze in a country where national income is growing and agricultural supply has moved ahead of the rate of population growth. The consumer is saying that he has a higher income and he wishes, with rapid progress in farm technology and the ability of food supply to increase rapidly, relatively more of the national resources to be used for nonfarm goods.

The structural changes encouraged or brought about by economic growth cause the absolute magnitude of certain resources to decline. Labor, and land in some cases, actually declines in total agricultural employment in most advanced countries. Apparently this process also will begin in other countries as further economic development takes place. The displacement of labor is directly an effect of changes in the relative quantities and prices of capital and labor under economic growth. As economic growth mounts to high levels, capital increases relatively in supply and its price becomes lower compared to the price of labor. Compared to the cost of labor in the United States, fertilizer is now only about one-third as costly as in the period 1935-1939; farm machinery and all other input items are only one-half as costly.

The human resources are consequently displaced for two reasons: (1) Capital in the form of mechanical power and machines is substituted directly for labor; each person can handle more acres and animals with this advanced capital equipment. (2) Indirect substitution of biological innovations for labor takes place. This second source of labor displacement is much less obvious than the first, but it has important bearing on total labor in agriculture. Innovations or new forms of capital, such as improved crop varieties and livestock breeds, insecticides, and others that increase output per animal or acre, cause less labor to be required per unit of product marketed. Equally, with mechanical forms, the new biological forms of capital allow agricultural employment to decline in absolute magnitude.

This process is encouraged under economic growth through shifts in the price of capital as compared to the price of labor. At low stages of economic growth, as in North America 150 years ago or in India currently, the supply of labor is large relative to the supply of capital, thus making the price of labor lower than the price of capital. Hence, labor technology is used and the inputs of farming are composed mostly of labor. A century back, 75 percent of all inputs in United States farming was labor and only 25 percent was capital. Now the situation is reversed; the proportion is 75 percent capital and 25 percent labor. Under labor technology, farms are small and large portions of the labor force and population are engaged in farming. Farms are small because of the small capital used. Based on labor technology, great-scale economies or cost advantages do not exist and small farms evidently have a strong economic base.

Thus, in highly advanced economies, two major agricultural problems can come about. While both are closely related to economic development, they differ considerably in their nature and degree of permanence. The first is the surplus problem, with the tendency of output and commodity supply to progress faster than consumer demand for food. It arises because the new forms of capital lift the restraint of land on production. This problem is so much more obvious that the second problem tends to be overlooked as equally basic. The second results from the relative change that takes place in resource prices under economic development, with its effect on the substitution of capital for labor. It is further expressed in cost advantages that attach to the size of the producing unit, and hence in the number of farm units and families able to exist in a competitive but slowly growing industry such as agriculture. As the supply of capital increases relative to labor and substitution takes place, scale economies or cost advantages are realized by larger farms because of the fixed costs that attach to capital items such as tractors and machines. Thus, economic growth calls for larger units if farms are to have enough volume to attain low unit costs. There is then room for fewer farms.

Certainly the major and basic adjustment problems of United States agriculture revolve more around the second set of forces than around the surplus problem. Even if the surplus problem is solved, either overnight or in a decade, the major problem related to economic growth and relative changes in resource prices would remain. Any solution would still require or encourage a shift in the farm resource mix to a richer proportion of capital, a greater reliance on management, a numerically smaller labor force, and larger and fewer farms.*

At higher stages of growth, technical improvement and the substitution of capital for labor also receive increased momentum from the private sector. At low stages of growth, when labor is the main resource used, private business has only a small market for capital items. Accordingly, it conducts little research for improvement of agriculture, and this function must be carried by the public. But with advanced economic growth and resource prices that favor the substitution of capital for labor, there is a large market for capital items. The capital is represented by fertilizer and insecticides, machinery, improved seeds, and other such products. The more productive these prove to be, the greater the quantity industry can sell to farmers. Private industry then conducts more research on improved farm technology and invests heavily in communicating the results to farmers, in order to sell more production materials to agriculture. Greater impetus thus is given to technological advances, growth in farm output, the substitution of capital for labor, and the reduction in the farm labor force. This set of forces undoubtedly will keep the productivity and output of American farms moving ahead rapidly. Private industry now is investing more than the public sector in establishing and communicating new technical knowledge for agriculture.

As output expands and farm prices and income become depressed, family income and resource earnings in agriculture could be maintained under only one condition; namely, great mobility or outward flow of resources from agriculture so that income of those remaining moves to the previous level, or to the level of the nonfarm economy. The latter could be attained through (1) fewer people in agri-

---

* Almost the same process has been going on in the structure of food retailing, as the corner grocery store has been replaced by the giant supermarket.

culture among whom income is divided, (2) a rise in the marginal productivity of those resources remaining, and (3) a restraint or dampening on output as resources leave.

Unfortunately, resources are highly fixed in agriculture in the short run and remain on hand at full production. Labor remains because of the immobility of farm personnel. But various forms of capital, such as barns and tractors, also are immobile in the short run; they have little transfer value to other sectors. In this sense, they are much like farm labor, whose skills have little use elsewhere. As resources, they are not flexible in moving to other industries where relative consumer demand is higher. They, too, stay on in agriculture contributing to a product that brings them a low return. The low mobility of resources is obviously one of the problems to be overcome or offset in solving agriculture's problems. Looking at society as a whole and in the long run, we might say that resource mobility *is* the agricultural problem.

As we have seen, agriculture in the United States is faced with a particular set of problems stemming from the process of economic development and the stage of maturity in our economy. New capital technology, encouraged by the advance of science and the lowered real price of capital, allows more food to be produced with less labor. Yet little additional food per person will be used without a sharp reduction in its price. The result is lower income for the farm sector in the absence of offsetting farm policy and greater mobility of resources.

Without an appropriate set of policies, we cannot be certain that the sum outcome is positive. There are many more consumers than farmers. Yet we have no measuring stick that can guarantee that positive gains to consumers are greater than negative outcomes for food producers. The sum of a positive and a negative is not necessarily positive. Perhaps our meandering in government farm programs in recent decades has been a search for positive-sum policies: to continue the advance of agriculture for the benefit of consumers, but also to provide appropriate means of compensating farmers for the losses they otherwise experience. This is a basic policy problem.

PART II

PUBLIC
POLICIES AND
AGRICULTURAL
GOALS

CHAPTER III

Government and Agriculture

People viewing the large Treasury outlay for farm programs frequently make the plea, "Get the government out of agriculture." They ask that "we return to the good old days" when the public did not intervene in the markets on behalf of agriculture. But was this ever so?

Government policies for agriculture are not something new. Almost since its birth as an independent nation, the United States has had very active and purposeful public policies on behalf of agriculture. All of them have been aimed directly at improving the economic position of farmers, although indirectly they frequently have had equal or overriding objectives resulting in gain to consumers and the public generally.

One overall set of programs was initiated early in the nation's history when population, per capita incomes, and food demand were growing rapidly. These policies had the effect of providing gains to both consumers and producers at that time, thereby generally assuring positive-sum outcomes.

This general policy approach has been extended to the present. However, because of national economic development, taken alone it can no longer assure gains to both food producers and consumers. Mainly in the last three decades, therefore, another set of policies has been initiated and implemented directed at compensating farmers to offset their income squeeze.

For convenience, the two sets of policies may be called *developmental policies* and *compensation policies.* The first set, initiated early in the nation's history and continued vigorously through the present, are directed toward improving efficiency and increasing the amount and productivity of resources used on farms—with the net result not only of more output per worker and acre but also of more total output for the industry. The other set, compensation policies, were initiated especially in the 1930's in an attempt to improve farm income through direct payments to farmers, reducing output and marketings to increase prices, and related means. They continue to serve as nonmarket means of compensating farmers for, or offsetting the effects of, the inelastic demand for food and the depression of income that results when production capacity or output advances more rapidly than population and market outlets.

A third set of programs, which do not have either of these purposes, are *regulatory policies,* such as the Pure Food and Drug Act. They are mainly aimed at protection of consumer health and welfare.

Early developmental policies, those first initiated by the public and aimed at increasing farm income through lower resource prices and greater output, were designed by the government to distribute the public domain. The resource of concentration was land. The government used its own direct and nonmarket means to keep the supply of land large and its cost to farmers low. This same method of increasing the supply and lowering the cost was extended to capital and knowledge resources. It is still in effect today.

When the supply of a resource is kept large and its price is lowered through government action, more of it will be used. The result almost always will be a larger output. But the larger output will increase farm income only under certain conditions of demand.

Just as now, there were debates over the extent to which the lot of farmers should be decided in the market or by government aids. Hamilton would have sold the public's land to private investors who then would have marketed it among farmers. Jefferson, whose philosophy triumphed, advocated distributing the land at low prices through government machinery. In some cases farmers paid a small price to the government for the land; in other cases, especially under the Homestead Act but also under other arrangements, they were given the land by the public. Perhaps it would be better to say that they acquired the land directly from the government at no monetary cost, since they did have to meet certain requirements. They had to live on it, develop it, plant trees, and fulfill other obligations. But the supply of land was kept large through purchases from foreign nations and by other means.

Once the precedence of public land distribution was established, no other major means was used; the method was accepted as the American way. The immediate purpose was to provide land to farmers at low or zero prices. The secondary purpose was development of the nation and securing its territories. Had the government turned to a procedure of sales and distribution through the market, pioneer farmers undoubtedly would have protested with muskets in their hands. A few did so in any case when they were pressed to relinquish land they had taken over before public machinery could be extended to new territories.

During this early period of agricultural policy, farmers'

and public benefit were mutual. Farmers were given land or obtained it at a low price directly from the government. Output increased rapidly. Farming in total produced more income (an extremely important aspect of national development since the majority of the nation's resources were in agriculture), and a larger food supply at reasonable prices was secured for consumers.

While not all farmers could live on the frontier and gain from free or low-priced land distribution, those who tended the fields of settled regions also gained from the expanding market. The value of the land that they obtained at low prices appreciated rapidly. It allowed inheritances typically within the same generation and always from one generation to the next, with a capital gain that in turn provided a basis for loans and capital to increase resources and improve production.

Mutual gains, a guarantee of a positive-sum outcome since the results were "plus" for all major groups, was possible because of the state of food demand and economic development in the early period of the nation. First, the population was increasing rapidly—by over 80 percent in each twenty years of the period 1790-1870 and by over 50 percent in each twenty years of the period 1870-1910. Second, people were poor by today's standards, and their diets were not varied. However, per capita income was rising, also about 80 percent every twenty years over much of the same period, and demand elasticity was high enough to bring greater per capita expenditure on food as its real price declined. Third, a slow but steady process of industrialization led more people away from farms and toward towns and cities where they produced less of their own food. With a highly elastic market, developmental policies to keep resource prices low and farm output growing could bring greater income to farmers. Starting from low incomes and limited food per person, the price elasticity of demand undoubtedly was high enough so that more output at a lower price could increase total farm income. This is the necessary situation if a vigorous developmental policy for agriculture is to increase farm income.

Of course, the majority of the population was rural during the period that developmental policies had their main positive contribution in altering farm income. Rural residents in the national population ranged from 95 percent in 1790 to 54 percent in 1910. It was only in 1920 that the urban exceeded the rural population. Most of the food consumers were also food producers. It thus was difficult, and perhaps unnecessary, to distinguish between policies that were aimed at one or the other of these two major groups.

As long as public policy and national development could provide farmers with low-priced land and eventual capital gains, they asked for little else. They did not like the high cost of borrowed capital and low prices of short-lived "market gluts." However, the main ingredients of farming were land and labor. Very little capital was used and high interest rates were not greatly restraining.

Relative to the times, early government programs were somewhat similar to one in recent decades that would have given farmers a few shares of IBM stock. Large capital gains resulted simply from holding the asset while the market grew. It is much easier to find a policy that pleases people when an industry is expanding rapidly and labor is being drawn into it and the main government aid is in getting more production power to farmers. Under present-day circumstances, when the level of economic development, rapid technological improvement of agriculture, and the restrained rate of demand growth pushes labor out of agriculture and limits income gains from greater output, agreement on farm policy is much more difficult.

But with complete settlement of the Western and Southwestern regions of the nation, the national domain approached exhaustion. Land was no longer readily available for further extension of this first developmental policy for agriculture. (The public, however, still makes some land available through irrigation projects of the Bureau of Reclamation.)

Since the first policy had been so successful, the public again turned to a developmental policy as its major aid to agriculture; namely, the supplying of new technical knowledge. Public creation of research and educational facilities became the second major step. Thus around the period of the Civil War, state agricultural colleges and the U.S. Department of Agriculture were created for the purpose of conducting research and education to help farmers increase yields and output on their existing land.

As in the case of land, the American public provided this resource at a zero or very low price to farmers; it socialized research by setting up its own facilities to generate new knowledge and communicate it at no cost to farmers. Nevertheless, the main momentum in increasing yields and productivity and further developing agriculture immediately after creation of the agricultural colleges and research facilities still came from settlement of free lands, the capital gains flowing from free land settled earlier, and the general effects of public education.

American society continued to enlarge its investment in generating new technology for agriculture. From the outset, new state agricultural colleges were created every year or two. The U.S. Department of Agriculture was consolidated and expanded into cabinet status in the 1880's. The Hatch Act of 1887 provided more federal funds to create new or additional experiment stations or research centers for agriculture. State and federal appropriations for agricultural research and education increased almost every year. The Smith-Lever Act of 1914 created the agricultural extension services, special educational facilities with technical experts located at the state agricultural colleges and at local levels, to carry more information directly to farmers. The Smith-Hughes Act of 1917 provided federal funds to create vocational agricultural departments in high schools. These special programs, making up the majority of the curriculum for participating students and prospective farmers, have been very influential in improving the technology of farming.

In fact, public appropriations for the purpose of developing new knowledge and extending it free to farmers have almost doubled in each decade from the initiation of the programs up to the present. The volume of new technology has been on a rapid upswing over the last fifty years and, having attained the greatest height of any place in the world, it is now increasing more rapidly than ever. Private industry also has boosted its investment in producing new knowledge for farming. In fact its budget for this purpose, allowing a greater demand for the machines, chemicals, and other inputs it sells to agriculture, is now greater than the public's share.

Aside from policies leading to rapid settlement of public lands, the American public's investment in generating and communicating new knowledge to improve farming has been the most striking development in world agriculture. These public facilities have been outstandingly effective in developing new technologies and getting them put into practice on farms. Of course, technical improvements represent new forms of capital such as improved seeds, fertilizers, machines, insecticides. Also the adoption of these new technologies has been greatly encouraged by the stage of economic development in the United States, which maintains a low price of capital relative to labor.

Socialization or supplying of new agricultural technology through public means was a developmental policy because it kept the price of the knowledge resource at a zero or low level. A greater supply and a low price for a resource always tend to increase its use and hence to result in greater output. The greater output can increase total farm income only if demand is elastic (Example A, Chapter I). It is likely that the equivalent of an elastic demand for farm products existed up to around 1910. The high demand elasticity came from a continued high rate of population increase, growth in per capita incomes of a population that started from a low base, and the international debtor position of the United States, which encouraged large exports of food.

There were also other developmental policies that aimed to increase the supply and lower the price of resources and encourage output. The Bureau of Reclamation, established in 1902 and still in operation, facilitated public investment in irrigation projects and water storage. The land and water facilities so developed have been distributed at a low cost to settlers. Nearly 10 million acres of arid and semiarid land have been put under irrigation by this government agency.

By 1912, the public began active discussion of public means to lower the cost of capital through reduced interest rates. The time was appropriate for these considerations, since the new technologies now being adopted by agriculture increasingly represented capital items. Accordingly, the Farm Loan Act of 1916 gave rise to the Federal Land Bank System, created specifically for supplying credit at lower costs to farmers. The public credit facilities acquired funds from society at large and disbursed loans to farmers at lower interest rates. As in the case of research and extension of knowledge, the public created its own machinery for this purpose. These facilities still exist and public credit agencies, organized under a special type of farmer cooperative, supply capital side-by-side with private credit firms. These capital-supplying and pricing activities by the public were extended through the Federal Intermediate Credit Banks in 1923. Subsequent public agencies, created to increase the supply of capital and lower its price, include the Farm Credit Administration and the Production Credit Administration in 1933, the Resettlement Administration in 1935, the Farm Security Administration in 1937, and the Farmers' Home Administration in 1946.

All these public and semipublic agencies, or their modern-day counterparts, still have as their basic purpose supplying credit at a favorable price to farmers. As in other developmental policies that provide lower prices for resources, these public facilities act to increase the income of farmers through lowering acquisition costs for resources and allowing them to produce more.*

Developmental policies also have been represented in other government programs. The Soil Conservation Service provides free technical help to farmers in improving their land and preventing erosion. While some of this aid has purely the effect of conserving the soil for the future, the majority of it increases yields and productivity at the present. Under various agencies since the 1930's and currently, the public subsidized farmland improvement practices. Hence, the cost of materials for draining land, developing irrigation, applying fertilizer, and conserving moisture has been lowered. Many of these practices help increase output of the individual farmer.

He can increase income from this practice if enough other farmers do not follow the same route to greater supplies of farm products. If they do, the inelastic demand will once again bring a lower total revenue to all.

Almost all new farm technologies increase output relative to resources employed. Because of the competitive nature of farming, the individual farmer must adopt them if he is to "stay in the race,"—that is, keep his costs low enough so that he can compete successfully with other farmers in producing an undifferentiated commodity.

Of course, even though all farmers on the average have lower incomes when more is produced and sold in a competitive market under an inelastic demand, *some* farmers can gain while others lose. Farmers who increase their output by a greater percentage than prices decline gain in income even

---

* On the other hand, the greater output that must be sold under an inelastic demand could be expected to lower income of all farmers in aggregate.

though the rest have lower incomes. Hence, farmers with sufficient capital for expansion may prefer only developmental policies. Farmers who lose, because they have less capital and cannot increase output as fast as prices decline, evidently prefer compensation policies. Here is a major basis for disagreement on farm policy, one that is very real in American farm politics.

Obviously, the United States was never without a major policy for agriculture. It stepped in and provided services and functions for agriculture that in other economic sectors were left to the market. Furthermore, the early developmental policies were not temporary measures. Extended to the present, they are highly efficient in improving the technology of agriculture and allowing the industry to produce more food with less land and labor, thus adding to national progress. They do require more capital, with the effects both of replacing labor and increasing investment for farming.

This set of policies for agriculture would have its counterpart in industry if the public set up research institutes in each state to develop more efficient methods of producing television or automobiles, retailed this knowledge free to all potential producers, and supplied them with materials and credit at reduced cost so that they could initiate or extend production. But if the public threatened to introduce these measures for industry, a barrage of protests and counteractions would immediately arise—even though the instrument is considered the "American way" for agriculture. In fact, so efficient have been these developmental policies in increasing farming efficiency and maintaining a large food supply that nations from all over the world send specialists to visit the United States to study this marvel and learn how to duplicate it.

In the early setting of national economic development these developmental policies are consistent with greater income to the agricultural industry. But this setting cannot continue forever under rapid and continuous national economic growth. A stage is finally attained in consumers' incomes in which their desire for food is largely filled. Further progress in rapid resource development and food supply can then become inconsistent with greater aggregate farm income, unless a market is developed simultaneously to go with the greater output. This stage of national economic development was clearly being approached by the early 1920's. Only then was the second major agricultural development policy, public production of improved technology, beginning its large social payoff in greater farm productivity and lower real prices of food. The returns to society at large from these developmental policies have been high. Estimates suggest the payoff on investment in agricultural research and education alone to be 50 percent, often running to 700 percent on individual investments.*

World War I served to create a new and wider market for goods. But around 1920, after the worldwide wartime demand for United States food products slackened, there was an abrupt change in the conditions that had given rise to high demand elasticities. Demand certainly became highly inelastic in the 1920's. The population increased less rapidly. The United States was now a creditor nation and enacted tariff policies that invited retaliation and reduced our farm exports. Most important, the level of personal income was now such that the first urgency of the well-fed American consumer was not for more food but for other goods and services of a wealthier society. Hence, the developmental policies could no longer be aimed primarily at farmer gains. The main beneficiary now became the consumer. He got a larger supply and variety of food with a reduction in its real price. The new technology created for agriculture was represented by capital items that substituted for labor. This labor could be released from, or forced out of, agriculture

---

* See Earl O. Heady, *Agricultural Policy Under Economic Development* (Ames: Iowa State Universtiy Press, 1962), pp. 599-602.

to be made available for the more rapid growth of other industries consistent with the ranking of consumption urgencies by a high-income society.

While many agricultural leaders still supposed demand to be elastic, some farmers did identify and recognize the change in the market environment. They turned to self-help measures largely representing attempts to increase demand but with some emphasis on production control.

Large national cooperatives for major commodities were created in the late 1920's in the hope that demand could be expanded through promotion and quality control of farm products. It was also hoped that price could be improved through more orderly marketing and market management or supply control. In previous decades, farmers had organized cooperatives as a means of breaking grain and other market monopolies. Now, however, interest arose in using cooperatives—allowing orderly marketing—to obtain possible price and income gains under supply control procedures. The plan was an attempt to create pools into which the product would move, with a reduced amount moving directly to the domestic market.

These self-help attempts based on large-scale commodity cooperatives were generally unsuccessful. Farmers were too great in number, too widely dispersed, and produced commodities serving too nearly as substitutes for each other. Futhermore, farmers were not easily organized into a voluntary group that could control production. Little could be done to control markets without control on production. Most planned commodity marketing organizations never got under way and others proved of short life. On a voluntary basis, groups of farmers would get together and agree to reduce output, but as individuals they would go home and plant more.

The inability of self-administered agricultural programs to increase demand and restrict supply caused farmers to look to the government for mechanisms that would overcome the inherent difficulties of voluntary organizations. Although some farmers, then as now, opposed turning to government for organizational aid and market power, major sentiment favored this direction and the general approach was incorporated in policy legislation of the late 1920's. Congress passed, and President Coolidge vetoed, the McNary-Haugen two-price plan in both 1927 and 1928. Under it, domestic sales of major crops would have been restricted to amounts bringing the world price plus the domestic tariff; the remaining output was to be sold in the world market.

While it did not pass, the philosophy underlying the McNary-Haugen plan provided the foundation and precedent for policy legislation that followed. The Agricultural Marketing Act of 1929, creating the Federal Farm Board, was passed as a first formal step toward a public compensation policy for agriculture. This act provided for lessening speculation, preventing inefficient and wasteful methods of distribution, aiding organizations or producers for unity of effort in marketing, creating producer-owned cooperatives, and assisting in the control of surpluses. Congress appropriated $500 million to finance the cooperative marketing associations under the Board. Loans were made to help keep market supplies down, but lack of measures for production control and the crash of 1929 thwarted these effects. Also, the $500 million provided was insufficient to demobilize marketings and raise prices.

The abrupt turn to compensation policies followed the great economic crises of 1929-32. Under the New Deal, the Agricultural Adjustment Act of 1933 provided major funds and machinery for initiating these policies. They included means that (1) compensated for, or offset, the effects of developmental policies or other forces that caused output to increase rapidly and prices to drop abruptly under an inelastic demand for food and (2) gave direct payments to farmers to compensate for depressed prices and incomes.

Developmental policies in the form of government provision of research, education, credit, irrigation development, soil conserving services, and certain other means of production were continued. They still make important contributions to the welfare of consumers and national economic growth. Compensation policies, still in effect today, were attempts to provide some means whereby farmers could make use of these developmental contributions and also gain, or at least not suffer sacrifices, from their efforts.

Perhaps only a few people actually realized that the developmental policies used after 1920 and the compensation policies put into effect in the 1930's are in conflict with each other in relation to their expected effect on output and on the mass income of farmers. Under conditions of inelastic demand, developmental policies will lessen market revenue since increased output can be sold only with sharp price reductions (unless they are used only to an extent that growth in output just equals growth in population and foreign demand). As we have seen, because of the low income elasticity of demand for food, gains in per capita incomes in the United States result in an extremely small increase in the demand for food—even when prices are falling. Thus, developmental policies increasing output lead to a need for further compensation policies to sustain farm income.

Developmental policies do need to be pursued to maintain the growth in agricultural efficiency, partly to aid national economic growth but especially to provide a margin of safety in the food supply for future generations. Yet if they are pursued for these purposes, it is reasonable that the public provide compensation policies that prevent major sacrifices on the part of farm families; otherwise, all the benefit goes to nonfarm families. The important question is the form that these compensation policies should take if they are to accomplish their objectives and not (1) impose a permanent maladjustment in the structure of agriculture or (2) require large public expenditures without ever solving the problems to which they are directed. Numerous types of compensation policies can be used. Many have been in force over the last several decades.

By 1932 the depression that began in 1929 had brought farm prices to extremely low levels. While other industries closed their shops or decreased output in response to depression prices, agricultural output continued full blast—but prices fell even lower. Drastic measures were required to prevent bankruptcy of millions of farmers. The legislation that was provided was based on the belief that the problem was of short-run nature and that as soon as the depression was whipped, full employment would restore farm prices and erase income problems. However, the compensation policies put into effect at this time were generally continued into the postwar period of full employment, when it became increasingly apparent that agriculture's problems were largely structural, stemming from the rapid advance of the industry itself.

The Agricultural Adjustment Act of 1933 (AAA) provided the mold for compensation policies. Current policies basically still rest on this act or amendments to it. The Federal Farm Board was liquidated in 1933 and the new organization set out to eliminate what was believed to be its limitations; namely, that storage programs alone to keep products off the market were ineffective without production controls to limit supply. The AAA initiated direct means to reduce the acreage and output of crops. A companion policy instrument, the Commodity Credit Corporation (CCC), was created to provide for loans and storage to reduce marketings when production was too large. It too still exists.

Under the AAA program beginning in 1933, funds were provided for the government to contract with farmers to reduce the acreage of the basic crops: wheat, cotton, corn, rice, tobacco, and peanuts. Other commodities have since been added to this list. Millions of farmers, encouraged by direct or benefit payments, entered into these contracts. The no-tion at trial was that illustrated in Example B of Chapter I. If demand for a commodity is inelastic, a reduction in output and higher prices will increase the revenue or income from it. Marketing quotas limiting the amount of crops that could be sold by the farmer also were applied to cotton and tobacco. Payments were made for plowing up some cotton to reduce the acreage for harvest in 1933.

The government also bought up some pigs and destroyed them to reduce the supply of pork. This action led almost immediately to a heated public controversy, shaming the government for killing the little animals. Partly for this reason—but also for others—government programs have never again attempted to "kill the little pigs." Evidently, the public is in accord with killing hogs to increase the meat supply and welfare of consumers, but not with killing little pigs to increase the income of farmers. This incident illustrates two facts about farm policies. First, the values or philosophies we hold have important bearing on what policies can be used. Second, people are sometimes inconsistent, to say the least, when it comes to farm policies.

After the original AAA was declared unconstitutional, the Agricultural Adjustment Act of 1938 was passed which provided the same general means of compensation. This act and other amendments over time, serve as the general framework of today's compensation policies and provide for (1) acreage allotments to reduce the acreage and production of crops, with payments to compensate farmers who participate, (2) marketing quotas limiting the amount all farmers can sell of a particular crop, providing that two-thirds of the producers vote favorably in a referendum called for these purposes, and (3) marketing agreements permitting farmers and food processors to organize, without prosecution under antitrust laws, for purposes of limiting marketings of agricultural products. The act provided for conservation payments to farmers who would put certain soil conservation practices into effect. Parity payments were also made to farmers to make up the differences between (1) prices actually received for basic commodities and (2) the level of "parity prices," a level defined to give farm products the same purchasing power they had enjoyed over the period 1910-1914 when markets favored them.

The underlying purposes of this legislation were clear: to reduce the output and marketings, as a means of increasing farm prices and revenue because food demand is inelastic; to transfer funds from the Treasury to farmers as a direct means of compensation and income supplementation. The nation now invests more funds in these means than ever before.

Storage programs to lessen marketings and raise prices were also enacted. The Commodity Credit Corporation, initiated as a temporary measure in 1933, was provided more power and finances as a policy tool in later years. It became a chief means for raising prices, given the level of production, and it has served as the government's arm for handling acquisition, storage, and sales of surplus commodities. It grew in importance for these purposes after short crops in 1934 and 1936, and because production control programs were not entirely effective up to the war. Similarly, it has performed an important role in handling surplus production during the 1950's and 1960's.

As a price-supporting mechanism, it serves this function through "nonrecourse" loans. In other words, a farmer who does not want to sell his crop can obtain a loan against it from the CCC. If the loan rate, based on the parity price level, is above the market price, he can later choose to turn the crop over to the CCC as full payment of his loan. The farmer effectively receives a higher price than he would if he sold in the free market, thereby realizing a subsidy or premium equal to the difference between the market price and the loan rate. The CCC acquires ownership, stores it, and thereby cuts back on marketings to hold up prices. If surplus is maintained, it is obvious that the CCC must lose on its transactions, since it must dispose of its holdings at market prices that are less than loan rates plus storage costs. While it did not have large realized losses prior to World War II, the CCC has had large losses in postwar years and sometimes has built up very large stocks in order to avoid selling the crops it holds. It is termed a corporation but the basic function is not to make profits. On the contrary, its losses from supporting or raising farm prices are covered by the Treasury.

Of the numerous other public compensation programs that were inaugurated before World War II, several were attempts to increase the demand for farm commodities. The Federal Surplus Relief Corporation, later the Federal Surplus Commodities Corporation, was created in 1933 for these and other purposes. It functioned then, as now, to distribute surplus commodities to needy families and for school lunch programs. Hence, it also had the commendable purpose of upgrading diets of persons who might be deficient in this basic aspect of living. Products acquired and distributed have included pork, butter, wheat, eggs, milk, flour, beans, cheese, rice, fruit, vegetables, and turkey. Modifications of the program have been made over time, through the Food Stamp plan and other legislation. In 1966, more than a million families were receiving some free food.

Since food under these programs is provided free or at prices below the market, the difference between this price and the price at which commodities are acquired by the CCC comes from the United States Treasury.

Some programs of the 1930's, especially those relating to credit, were emergency measures to avert bankruptcy of masses of farmers. Most authorities and the public believed that once the depression was over and people went back to work, the demand for food would rise to levels that would eliminate the huge surplus of production and extremely low farm prices and incomes. In short, the entire complex of programs was expected to be temporary.

War conditions did eliminate most of the problems of surpluses and did increase farm prices and incomes. Farming was more profitable in the late part of the war and the period immediately following than it had ever been. Part of the boost in demand and prices came from the large food exports made to the nation's allies during the conflict—thus, once again, a new and wider market was opened up to our farmers. The war-torn countries required a few years to restore their agricultural production, but once they did, the temporary increase in demand for American products subsided.

United States farm productivity had risen rapidly since the 1930's and continued to do so in the postwar period, as farmers' high incomes generated savings to acquire more capital technology. Hence, by the early 1950's, food production once again was pressing hard on demand. It was now obvious that the United States farm problem, rather than being temporary, was a long-run one stemming from an advanced economy and further economic growth and requiring fundamental changes in the structure of agriculture.

In attempts to solve these problems, however, the nation reactivated the set of public programs first initiated in the 1930's, which supposed the problem to be only one of temporary surplus producing capacity. While they have been changed somewhat, especially with additional programs for disposal of surpluses in other countries, the means now in use are largely these earlier policies. Again they are aimed at compensation, either in (1) offsetting increases in farming productivity through acreage control programs, marketing quotas, and expanded demand through public means or (2) direct payments from the Treasury and price supports to offset income losses through the market.

The public policy instruments, initiated originally to deal with the emergency of the 1930's, have not eliminated the long-run and basic structural problems of agriculture.

They have failed to do so because they do not come to grips with the basic causes of the problems—namely, the forces unleashed by a high state of technical and economic development in agriculture and the national economy and an insufficient degree of mobility in agricultural resources. At times the policy means used have even been inconsistent with the objectives that they were expected to accomplish.

The public continues to invest in two sets of policies for agriculture: developmental policies that lead to advances in productivity and output, and compensation policies to offset the effect of greater output and structural changes on farm income. The developmental policies, augmented by the forces of national economic growth, are desirable from the standpoint of national welfare. At the same time, it is only logical that there be compensation policies to provide farmers with some payoff for this contribution to the national welfare. This is one of the basic policy problems before American society and the commercial farm industry. The task, however, is to find efficient and politically acceptable means for providing compensation.

CHAPTER IV

Recent Policy
and Legislation

Farming has provided American society with some of its major problems in postwar years. As with other urgent national concerns, the nation has legislated vigorously and invested heavily in trying to solve them. The pain of the problem has certainly been lessened but the basis exists almost as much today as thirty years ago. There is one difference, however. Thirty years ago both farming and the national economy were in the midst of a major depression. Today the national economy is in a period of unprecedented prosperity and economic growth.

Agriculture's problems are no longer those of an emerging commerical farm industry in the midst of national depression. They are long-run problems that stem from continued high speed in national economic progress. Adjustments in farming are inevitable. The forces of national economic development, relative resource prices, and modern scientific knowledge are so strong that they will take farming to a new level of capital structure, size, and sophistication regardless of farm policies. Changes are going to be more rapid than before, and they are going to tear harder at the roots of the rural community as they draw the labor force of agriculture toward its lower bounds. While world food demand or need promises to alleviate the surplus problem somewhat, it will not lessen the trend to fewer farms and workers.

Why have we stayed with farm policies oriented more to conditions of the last depression than to the emerging pressures of economic progress and world conditions? There are several reasons. One is the stalemate and conflict among farm organizations on the types of policies they prefer. The American public has been willing to appropriate large funds to solve problems of farming, even though the farming population is only one-fifteenth of the nation's total. But farming, unlike labor and other industrial organizations, does not have a single national voice to represent it. Instead, there are several national farm organizations, each with its own members and its particular policy philosophy and goals. To some extent, the farm polices of these organizations have been in direct conflict with one another. Accordingly, with old farm policy legislation on the books, it apparently was easier to patch up and go down the same road, as Republican and Democratic administrations have done in the last fifteen years, than to create new policies consistent with national economic progress and agriculture's future in it. The geographic dispersion of farming and the fact that farms in different regions are often as different as manufacturers of toothbrushes and automobiles (even though their products are not), add to this lack of a community of interest.

But the most important reason why we have not yet devised policies to provide basic solutions to farm problems is that we have not had sufficient experience or knowledge to deal effectively with these extremely complex problems. There have been no precedents to follow because no other country has attained such a high level of economic development. Conditions simply crept up on us and so gradually that we did not realize that the environment had changed for agriculture. While we still had our eyes on past short-run contingencies, such as bad weather and temporary depressions, it became apparent that the forces of national economic development giving rise to major problems of United States agriculture were not temporary.

Capital technology flowing into United States agriculture over the last forty years allowed a 100 percent increase in output with 60 million fewer acres. This advance, the substitution of capital and technology for land, has been equivalent to the discovery of a new Pacific island twice the size of Iowa and composed completely of farmland. Even with growth in our own population and a doubling of exports, output could grow another 50 percent in the next fifteen years while another 20 million acres are freed from crop production.* This, too, is an unprecedented experience for large societies: Land has always been an increasingly scarce resource relative to population, and nations have been pressed to acquire or develop more of it.

Up to the 1920's, the nation had been accustomed to an agriculture that grew and absorbed more labor and land. It had emphasized policies that cheapened resources and led to greater output. But now the stream had suddenly shifted to a different course. Agricultural output could grow rapidly and consumers could still gain greatly from the farming advances. In the absence of some other type of public policy, however, farming in the aggregate no longer stood to gain. Because of the competitive nature of farming many farm

---

* We may, however, decide to broaden help on world food needs and bring some land back into production. These needs are discussed in Chapter VIII.

people either had to leave agriculture or expand their farms and output to maintain their income. If they could do either rapidly enough, they might gain from the changing structure; if they could not, the cost of progress fell on them.

Since the public, especially farm leaders, had little knowledge or understanding of these processes and their long-run nature, they turned to the short-run emergency policies. We use the term public and farm leaders, rather than government officials and Congressmen, because the policies that have been maintained are not those of a specific political party. While originated largely under the Democratic administration of the 1930's, most of those in use were applied equally by Republican and Democratic Administrations over the last sixteen years. Moreover, had the public completely rejected them, they could have been readily voted out with Congressmen and administrations.

The fact is, without the farm programs of the last two decades, farm prices and incomes would have been much lower. Farm families and rural communities would have suffered greater uncompensated losses for the benefit of the nation's consumers generally. While slowing down somewhat the rate of adaptation of farming to economic growth, farm programs of the last thirty years perhaps have only held change in farming structure to a rate that could be somewhat better assimilated by the agricultural and the rural community.

But short-run emergency programs designed to live out the next few years will not alleviate problems of potential surplus in the next decade, nor will they solve the problems brought about by the structural adjustment of agriculture. Most important, they overlook the broader problems of farm families and other people in rural communities.

Who are the families most likely to feel the major cost burden of agricultural progress? They are those with insufficient capital to expand operations and extend efficiency as rapidly as output presses on market prices. They are middle-aged and older families whose skills were developed largely around agriculture and whose age or lack of education provide them with few abilities to take along for employment in other industries. They are merchants and service workers in rural towns, especially the older ones, whose business declines and capital values melt away as farms grow larger and capital substitutes for labor, to create a smaller rural population.

Our big public outlays for farm programs, with their emphasis on the problems of surpluses and commercial farmers (a rightful concern since the public does invest in the economic progress of agriculture) have not had any important impact in alleviating the problems of persons displaced from agriculture, decaying rural communities, and the permanently poor of farming.

We can summarize rather quickly the postwar farm policies that have moved us from "where we were" to "where we are." Obviously, the distance between these two points isn't very far. Farming has changed a lot in thirty years, but farm problems and policies have not. With the emergence of postwar surpluses, defined as the ability of agriculture to produce more than the market will absorb at prices acceptable to farmers, we again adopted farm programs that fall in one or the other of the following conventional methods of compensating for greater agricultural productivity and decreasing farm income: (1) increasing demand to raise prices, with commodities in long supply being allocated to low-income families and school lunch programs and with the program also extended in the form of aid to low-income countries; (2) reducing acreage to check production and increase prices; (3) cash payments from the Treasury to farmers who reduce acreage; (4) immobilizing production by moving crops into private and government storage to reduce market supplies and increase prices; (5) nonrecourse loans, serving as price supports, to induce farmers to move commodities into storage; (6) marketing quotas to check production and raise prices; (7) miscellaneous programs such as conservation payments for shifting land, reducing output, and increasing prices.

Of course, in addition to these compensation policies, the developmental policies have been continued and increased. Public expenditures on agricultural research and education have more than doubled since the war. While private firms producing machinery, chemicals, and the like have not invested in compensation policies to offset the effects of greater output, their investment in research and development for agriculture has increased tremendously.

Policy approaches of great range and diversity have been proposed and debated in postwar years. Yet the political forces and congressional balances have always brought the policy or instrument mix back to the same basic set, even though the farm problem gave rise to some of the most severe sectional and party tussles in postwar years. The debates began in 1948 and 1949, after wartime demand subsided somewhat and before the Korean-generated increase in demand began. They subsided during the Korean conflict, as market conditions improved, but arose again as farm income began to skid in 1952. In general, during the postwar period Democratic administrations favored high price supports and Republican administrations favored low and sliding-scale (declining based on a moving average) supports. Of the three largest farm organizations, one favored entirely free markets at times, one favored high price supports, and one favored price supports but at a medium or two-price level.

The nonrecourse loans of the CCC had provided a means for supporting prices at higher levels than market prices; however, market prices for many commodities first broke below the support levels in 1948. (Price supports had been put at high levels during the war to encourage production.) Potatoes and eggs, commodities not well adapted to storage, were first to glut the market; a large amount of potatoes rotted and brought the problem of price supports to the fore.

As theory would suggest, when prices were held at a high level by supports, farmers were producing potatoes and eggs in enormous quantities. President Truman first asked for flexible price support levels, with a low floor when supply was large and a high floor when supply was short. The majority of Republican Congressmen and a few Democrats favored the flexible support level, but Republicans from the Corn Belt and Great Plains, a solid block of Southern Congressmen, and some from the West favored continuing high supports. High-level supports won. The Senate then passed a sliding-scale support level. A compromise bill finally resulted, with high-level supports to continue for a year and a half, followed by a sliding-scale level. The CCC was reinstituted as a chartered corporation in 1948 and, after several skirmishes over it and its relation to storage of surpluses and price levels, became an election issue causing several farm states to vote for President Truman and carry the election.

High price supports were returned during the Korean conflict and production limits were not used except for tobacco and peanuts. Price supports again were frozen at the high level, 90 percent of parity, through 1954 by legislation in 1952.

By 1953, sharp debate had again risen over the level of price supports. Demand for some commodities had declined quite sharply as early as 1952 when the Korean war drew to a close. By 1954, under high price supports, wheat surpluses began to build up rapidly. Hence, marketing quotas were imposed for wheat, with acreage cut back from 79 million acres to 62 million acres, although imposition of the higher support level would have required a cutback to 55 million acres. Each farmer was given an acreage allotment and was allowed to market an amount equal to the allotment multiplied times the average yield per acre.

The marketing quotas were put into effect after farmers voted for them by a great majority. Wheat prices were then supported at the high level being debated and in effect during the war. Farmers with small acreages, under fifteen acres, were exempted from the quotas. With 27 million acres planted to cotton in 1953, it became apparent that similar support levels would require a reduction to 17.5 million acres in 1954. A sharp conflict between growers in the West and South on the allocation of this allotment resulted in a cutback to only 22.5 million acres and a maximum reduction of 29.5 percent by any one state.

With prices supported at the high level, and with acreage cut back to a compromise level rather than the amount consistent with the high price supports, the CCC began acquiring heavy surpluses of wheat and cotton. But prices still declined, to the support level for basic crops and to undefined levels by commodities not eligible for supports. Since wartime requirements had subsided, production was outrunning demand and all basic crops but rice were under production control in 1954. President Eisenhower proposed abandoning high rigid supports and the use of sliding-scale levels on a step-by-step basis between years to cushion the decline from the high levels in effect. To help cushion the transition to lower price supports, he also proposed an appropriation of $1 billion for acquiring surplus commodities to be donated to other countries. This legislation was passed following sharp sectional and party clashes.

Subsequently, of course, prices declined but production remained great because supply controls were not very effective. These conditions led to the passing of the Soil Bank bill in 1956. While the expectation was to retire land from production of surplus crops, the general theme was "to put the land in the bank and save it until need was greater." The program allowed payments to farmers who voluntarily retired their land for a period of three to fifteen years. While farmers over the entire country could withdraw land from production, participation tended to concentrate in marginal regions. To prevent too much concentration, maximum withdrawal was specified by counties. Support prices were continued and commodities moved into public storage because market prices were lower than the price-support or CCC loan levels.

Production continued to outstrip demand because acreage controls on output were not great enough or were ineffective. Surpluses had begun to arise, especially in feed grains, because programs had allowed farmers in the South who withdrew their land from cotton to plant corn, oats, or barley. Similarly, wheat farmers could shift their "withdrawn land" to feed grains, and acreage reductions in the Corn Belt were offset by increases elsewhere and the rapidly expanding technology in feed grains.

Following the Korean war, the trend was steady during the 1950's: prices declined and farm income fell. Production continued to grow and public stocks held by the CCC mushroomed rapidly. Despite heavy overseas disposal, by 1959 the CCC held in storage $2.4 billion of wheat, $891 million of corn, and $706 million of grain sorghums. It also had large amounts of cotton. But the biggest problem was wheat. CCC holdings of wheat had grown from a smattering in 1952 to 1.2 billion bushels in 1959—more than a year's crop and twice as much as our annual domestic consumption.

The Feed Grain program initiated in 1961 also was a voluntary program. It provided for cash payments to farmers who would reduce their acreage of corn and similar crops by 20 percent. Participating farmers were eligible for a price support of $1.20 per bushel of corn instead of $1.06. In addition, a farmer could retire another 20 percent of his land and receive payments in corn, out of public-held stocks, equal to two-thirds of normal production on this land. Control was made stronger since the retired land could not be shifted to other crops, as had been the case of most acreage-reduction programs to this time. With this promise of high price supports and larger farm payments, plus the promise of some actual reduction in output, the program was popular with Congress and readily passed.

During previous control programs, starting in the 1930's and extending through the 1960's, acreage reduction had had little effect on production. Farmers more than made up for the smaller acreage by withdrawing their poorest land and using more fertilizer and new technologies on their better land. Partly to circumvent this effect, President Kennedy proposed a long-range plan that would impose strict marketing quotas on all crops. Control would not rest on acreage but on the bushels and pounds sold. Allotments in this form were held to amounts that would bring prices to the desired level in the market. Under this arrangment, farmers would get their higher income through the market and consumer prices rather than from the Treasury and taxes.

Opposition to the plan was vigorous on the grounds of politics, ideology, and economics. It was opposed by Southerners who feared they would be controlled by the Secretary of Agriculture rather than by farmers who might use more loopholes; by large farmers who feared their share of the market might be cut back too far; by livestock producers concerned with the price of feed grains; by the American Farm Bureau because of its general farm policy stance; and by numerous food-processing and farm groups. It was favored by the National Farmers' Union, the Grange, and the commodity organizations representing cotton, corn, wheat, peanuts, tung oil, and several dairying groups.

The plan did not get far. It was killed in the agricultural committees of both the House and Senate. Hence, reliance fell back on acreage reduction through payments to farmers for participation, the general type of program continued on into the 1960's. Through 1962, feed grain and cotton producers were being paid for holding land out of production on a voluntary basis. In contrast, wheat producers had been operating under marketing quotas voted upon themselves as a compulsory program. Each farmer had to restrict acreage and marketing without payments. Accordingly, when the issue again came to a vote in 1963, wheat farmers voted down compulsory marketing quotas.

Through voluntary controls with payment for farmer participation in the 1960's, it was possible to exercise some restraint on production. Acreage reduction was about great enough to keep up with increases in yield per acre as farmers turned to more fertilizer and improved technologies. Under these conditions, of course, farm programs became increasingly expensive, since more funds must be appropriated to offset improved technology and to keep farmers under participation as price levels are brought to higher levels. The higher price levels themselves encourage the use of more inputs and improved technology, thus increasing output on the remaining acreage.

In the United States, crop output per acre has grown by nearly 40 percent from 1952 to 1967. But with the control programs of the 1960's, plus the growing shipments of food as aid to less developed countries, the buildup of stocks that had taken place rapidly in the 1950's was checked. CCC price-support inventories, which had reached $7.7 billion in 1959, declined by 10 percent in 1965. Government wheat stocks declined about 40 percent while feed grain stocks declined by about one-third. An even larger reduction in stocks was made between 1965 and 1967, as foreign shipments increased and normal carry-overs came into sight.

The decline in government-held stocks came more through shipments to other countries as foreign aid, and through some domestic population growth, than through control of production in the United States. Production control had done little to reduce output but mainly caused acreages to be reduced enough to offset improvements in technology. Annual wheat production averaged 1.2 billion bushels in the period 1956-1960 and again in 1961-1965. However, exports increased from .5 billion bushels in the first period to .7 billion in the second period. Annual corn production increased from 3.7 billion bushels to 3.8 billion bushels in the two periods but exports increased from .2 billion to .5 billion bushels. Less change took place in cotton stocks. With production of 12.9 million bales in 1956-1960 and 15 million bales in 1961-1965, CCC stocks were at 7.4 million bales in the earlier period and 7.3 million bales in the later period. In total, while price-support inventories held by CCC grew from $1.3 billion in 1952 to $7.7 billion in 1959, they had declined to $7 billion in 1965. Public stocks were not reduced much up to 1965, but the buildup had been stopped—itself an accomplishment.

Of course, program costs to the public grow large under the kind of policies in effect during the last two decades. And the costs increase as programs are expanded to keep up with the improving technology. Production has been exceeding domestic consumption and commerical exports by about 9 percent in recent years, even with nearly 60 million acres demobilized from crops by production control programs. The excess was about the same proportion in the 1950's when foreign disposal and acreage diversion programs were smaller. In recent years, the total annual cost of all programs, direct and indirect, to support farm prices and income has averaged about $5.1 billion if we include foreign disposal. The cost of foreign disposal itself, initiated in 1954 and increasing ever since, approaches $2 billion. While a large part of foreign shipments go for "soft" or nonconvertible currencies of underdeveloped countries, the return per dollar of such shipments may never amount to more than 10¢.

Along with foreign disposal of surpluses, the United States also has had a domestic disposal program amounting to about $250 million with food going for school lunches and to needy families. But this program cannot increase demand to the extent of foreign disposal. One study indicates that if all persons in the United States ate nutritionally balanced diets, total value of food consumption need not increase at all if consumers were to shift from commodities where consumption is excess to those where it is deficit.*

Our review of farm policies in the last two decades emphasizes several facts. First, it is not easy to obtain consensus on agricultural policy because of conflicting interests of different sections of the country, different producer groups, competing farm organizations, and political parties. Second, the farm problem is yet a long way from solution and its high costs are going to continue until better agreement can be reached on long-run solutions. Even if it is solved through more foreign aid, the annual cost will remain quite high. Finally, the emphasis on production control, price supports, and foreign disposal is obvious, while little consideration in farm programs per se has been given to the problems of people in agriculture.

Many recent national programs relating to development of people and economic opportunity will have importance for agriculture and rural communities. They are somewhat in contrast to farm programs in their orientation.

Major farm policies since 1940 have focused on commercial agriculture. The problems of this sector are quite different in nature and degree from those of the chronically low-income or poverty sector. Incomes in the extreme poverty sector of agriculture, the 665,000 farm families who have sales less than $5,000 per year, stem from historic conditions that placed little capital and education in the hands of this particular group. These farmers sell so little produce and possess so few resources that price and production policies can provide them with little income gain. Even if programs increased their income by the same proportion as for all United States farmers, the addition would not take them near the income levels Americans generally consider con-

---

* J. M. Wetmore *et al.*, *Policies for Expanding Demand* (St. Paul: University of Minnesota Press, 1959).

sistent with national goals. These farmers contribute little to the national farm output and are not part of the general over-production or resource structure problems.

Like other industries, agriculture has some persons whose low incomes are caused by age, illness, and other hardships, but they are not the basis of its widespread low incomes. Of the 1.5 million farms with sales under $2,500, nearly two-thirds are in the South. The figures in the table below emphasize that the poverty problem in agriculture is related not only to the South, but also to the concentration of Negro families on farms in this region.

Median Incomes of Families, 1962

UNITED STATES	URBAN FAMILIES	RURAL NONFARM FAMILIES	FARM FAMILIES
All families	$5,755	$5,361	$3,104
White families	5,994	5,514	3,455
Nonwhite families	3,519	1,819	1,440
SOUTH			
All families	4,791	4,670	2,378
White families	5,320	5,053	2,813
Nonwhite families	2,583	1,686	1,448

To explain these extremely low incomes in the South, and particularly those of Negro families and poor white families in the mountain areas, we need to examine industrial, political, and historic causes. The problems of extremely low incomes in agriculture are best solved, over the long run, under the newly created antipoverty program and other national welfare programs administered under the Office of Economic Opportunity and the Department of Health, Education and Welfare rather than the Department of Agriculture. The solution, except for a few, is not to be found in the farm industry. Instead, it is to be found in education and training, in employment by industries outside of agriculture, and by facilities that connect people with jobs. Even if these problems were solved, the major problems of commercial agriculture would remain. Or, conversely, if the commercial farm problem were solved, the true poverty problem would remain.

We must give low-income families, and particularly their children, the educational and occupational opportunities that are consistent with their abilities, human rights, and growth opportunities in a wealthy society. Most of them were bypassed in economic and social legislation of previous decades. Attainment of these ends is not now the objective of farm policy. Indeed, a more logical and efficient allocation of national resources would be to spend somewhat less on development and compensation policies for commercial agriculture and to invest a great deal more in human resources and in solving the poverty problem of agriculture.

Recently, American society has provided legislation and appropriations directed toward creating greater economic opportunity for these disadvantaged groups. This economic and social policy places more direct emphasis on the individual or human resource than have most previous national policies. It contrasts with farm policy, which has had income improvement as its ultimate objective but has focused so heavily on improving plants and animals, payments revolving around land, output control, storage, and other items that benefits often are highly diluted before they reach the farm family. They become diverted through higher land values, CCC storage payments to grain-processing firms who have never sacrificed through the avenue of technical progress and inelastic demand, and compensation to beginning farmers who have never suffered in agriculture.

Most of these new national programs, although directed at urgent urban and civil rights deficiencies and problems, can have important spill-over effects for the rural community. These programs focus on improved income distribution, welfare, and economic opportunity, and as such they cannot help but benefit the rural community where the incidence of poverty and cultural disadvantage is more concentrated than in urban centers.

The Elementary and Secondary Education Act of 1965 provides funds for local school districts with some weighting toward those counties with a high concentration of poverty. This emphasis will help in some agricultural communities that have a high incidence of poverty. It will increase national educational capacity and help improve schools in poorer communities, but it will give no special buildup, as compared to city schools, in commercial farming communities where there is much need for upgrading education. The Higher Education Act of 1965 also has less direct meaning for rural communities in general but provides a Teachers' Corps to help inadequate schools in poor areas. This facility especially will help the youth of poverty communities, such as those in the sharecropping areas of the South and the subsistence farming areas of the Appalachians—as well as declining coal mining communities and urban slum areas. It will not provide necessary upgrading for the conventional commercial farm community.

One of the Community Action programs, Title IIB of the Economic Opportunity Act of 1964, in its provision for improving the reading, writing, and arithmetic skills of adults with limited education, also will aid poverty-concentrated farm communities but has less relevance for the commercial farming community. Operation Head Start, the largest direct OEO project of the Community Action program, serves in a similar, but somewhat remote, vein in providing summer schooling for children of limited opportunity ready to enter the first grade.

The Vocational Education Act of 1963 provides federal funds to be matched by the states in developing vocational education and technical training for high school graduates, long lacking in rural communities. How successful this program is depends on initiative and appropriations by the states; many farm states have historically been reluctant to appropriate funds in these directions. These funds do not fill the void in vocational training at the high school levels. Title V of the Economic Opportunity Act of 1964 provides community work and training projects simultaneously to create income, work experience, and training for the unemployed and needy. The commercial farm community without industry and lacking the conditions to develop it cannot claim aid to transform the skills of operating farmers who need retraining for trade occupations. However, this program again promises some relief to individuals in highly depressed communities, especially those less remote from the industrial complex of the nation.

The Jobs Corps, under Title IA of the Economic Opportunity Act, also provides promise for unemployed youth, unprepared for jobs or socially useful lives, in concentrated poverty areas of agriculture as well as those of cities. The Neighborhood Youth Corps serves somewhat similarly. The Manpower Development Training Act of 1962, under the Department of Labor, provides for training for underemployed and unemployed people. In relation to agriculture, it has had most relevance in subsistence and low-income farming areas bordering population centers, distressed coal mining communities, and other such areas, rather than over the more sparsely populated commercial farming regions.

The Small Communities Program of 1962, introduced under the U.S. Employment Service, has initiated occupational skill surveys for smaller communities to improve job opportunities in rural areas. To a great extent, the focus here is in developmental planning for the community, an asset for communities that have the conditions for development but of limited aid to the many geographically dispersed farm communities that lack these endowments.

Other recent welfare and development programs also have implications for certain rural communities. Some programs bring improved medical facilities to rural areas, public works and development programs to create employment (the Public Works and Economic Development Program of 1965 supersedes the Area Redevelopment Administration), provisions of the Farmers' Home Administration for improving rural housing, federal programs to help local communities build highways, airports, libraries, and other facilities. This legislation is directed at society generally, to help overcome the economic disadvantage that has been the continued lot of many communities.

These are general social programs, rather than policies directed at agriculture, as evidenced by their administration under the Department of Labor, Department of Health, Education and Welfare, and the Office of Economic Opportunity, rather than under the Department of Agriculture. They are not ideally adapted to handle the problems of labor displacement from the towns and farms in commercial farm communities. Their focus for agriculture is more nearly on the long-existing poverty sector of the farm industry, but only as a by-product of a national attack on poverty.

Although some programs do provide long-needed help in solving the problems of the further economic transformation of agriculture, more investment must be directed toward the unique problems of the rural community. Programs with greater orientation to urban centers will take too long to lift fully the restraints in economic opportunity that pervade many rural communities.

Recent national programs to alleviate poverty and increase the economic opportunity of society at large are people oriented. They divorce themselves entirely from the problems of the last depression and address themselves to the conditions that should exist for a society as rich as America.

But agricultural policy has not yet come to look far to the future or to broadening the economic opportunity of people by investing in them. Rather, it invests in land, to get it retired; in grain, to get it stored; in exports, to get products out of the country. The hope is that income will get back to farm people. It will for some but for others the path is so long and roundabout that they gain only a smattering of income for more education and individual improvement, the basic requirements for employment in a growing economy.

CHAPTER V

Goals for
Farm Policy

Numerous policies designed to get at the basic problems of agriculture have been tried; many more could be tried. Unfortunately, none has been accepted by all groups surrounding agriculture—and none will. But this does not mean that economically sound policies that appropriately consider the welfare and income of farm families are impossible. To the contrary, the nonfarm public need not worry about dissent among farm groups in bringing sensible policies to agriculture. With only 7 percent of the population in farming, and sharp conflicts in the policies they back, farm groups appear to be asking the general public to bring long-run solutions to the fore. This is a reasonable demand: The nonfarm population after all represents 93 percent of the country and it also foots the direct money bill for farm programs.

. . . .

Agriculture has four general farm organizations that largely compete with each other in policy proposals and implementation, as well as a large number of commodity organizations that promote the specific interests of the growers of individual products. Also, there are many agribusiness sectors around agriculture that sell inputs to it, buy from it, or store its products. Because the policy that might aid one of these groups may mean a loss to another, the farm industry does not have a single voice to speak for it, has no very definite long-run program goals, and cannot agree on a single major policy format to solve its basic problems.

The largest general farm organization is the American Farm Bureau which tends to represent larger farmers, to promote conservative policy oriented to the play of market forces, and to align itself with Republican legislation and administrations. Its viewpoints also tend to mesh with those of the National Association of Manufacturers and the U.S. Chamber of Commerce.

The National Farmers' Union is about one-third as large and tends to go along with the views of labor and the Democratic party. It has generally promoted supply control and high price supports while the Farm Bureau has opposed them. In general, when one of these organizations comes out for a particular policy, the other is against it.

The National Grange, also about one-third as large as the Farm Bureau, is the oldest of the nation's farm organizations. It pursues an independent course on policy matters, somewhere between the first two organizations, but it favors government policy, other than the free market, and thus frequently is on the side of the Farmers' Union.

The National Farm Organization, organized during the period of low prices in the 1950's, has an orientation quite different from that of the other general organizations. Its emphasis is on attaining bargaining power for farmers. Its major attempt so far has been to get farmers to hold their livestock off the market to force price increases. Of course, without production control, any price improvement during reduced marketings will be more than offset by the inelastic demand for these products and the fact that the animals only grow larger so that a greater volume hits the market after the barriers are removed. Members of the National Farm Organization have used picketing, and a frequent flare of violence, in trying to get farmers to hold livestock off the market; however, livestock is unlike products such as petroleum or shoes, since it keeps on eating and adding to costs even though it is already produced.

General farm organizations did put forth a solid front when the initial compensation policies were legislated in the 1930's. They served as the foundation of the farm bloc that was largely successful in obtaining national legislation to aid farmers. However, unlike business represented through such organizations as the National Association of Manufacturers or the U.S. Chamber of Commerce, or different labor organizations, which debate and compete but present a solid front when most basic policy issues related to their interests arise, farm organizations have not had unanimous consent for dozens of years. In some instances, farm organizations have agreed on ultimate ends but have been in serious conflict over means.

The farm commodity groups also differ on policy. Dairy cattle farmers have used marketing quota controls most widely for milk; beef cattle producers are most vigorously against production controls. Farmers who sell grain for cash tend to favor acreage controls on output, but livestock producers who buy grain for feed tend to be against them. Small farmers seem to favor cash payments and controls, as do some large cash crop farmers; but large crop-livestock farmers seldom participate. In the agribusiness sector, grain storage firms favor programs like those of the 1950's, when prices were supported, no restraints on productions existed, and the excess output was moved into warehouses for long periods. Manufacturers and distributors of fertilizer, chemicals, and machinery favor this type of policy against acreage controls that cause fewer cropped and fertilized acres. Limestone producers probably favor production control payments that use more of their product for the grass and forage planted on diverted acres. Earth movers lobby for direct payment programs that subsidize farmers to terrace and level their land.

Not only do all these groups conflict with one another on farm policies, but the economic and political interests of the rural areas also come into the picture. While farmers may accept diversion of farms from production through payments for participation, local businessmen oppose this scheme because it encourages farm families to close down operations and move away. Then, too, there is the power structure centered in rural towns that refuses to admit that society has now been transformed from one dominantly rural to one dominantly urban. In the legislation, including reapportionment to eliminate unfair representation, these groups take issue with a good many other policies, including some farm programs. They are not great champions of aid to education in rural communities or instruments that will improve migration and expand economic opportunity elsewhere for surplus labor in rural areas.

The political power of agriculture vanishes with economic growth, of course; development and the substitution of capital for labor means that farming eventually has a minor proportion of a nation's work force. With each laborer goes a family and a set of votes. While part of the labor formerly in agriculture now is in industry producing tractors, chemicals, and other inputs for farming, it is more likely to associate its voting interests with automobile workers than with farmers.

Yet while the voting majority is now far out of reach of agriculture, it still tends to be highly favored by the quantity of public funds legislated in its behalf. To some extent, the structure of congressional committees, with seniority predominantly in the hands of Congressmen from the rural South, the disproportionate representation of farm states in the Senate, and the restraints of rural power in redistricting for congressional seats, have all favored this allocation. Still, society has been lush in appropriations for agriculture.

But with reapportionment and increased legislation dealing with urban social issues, agricultural groups may well have to begin concentrating and agreeing on more efficient long-run policies. Competition over funds for total national and international purposes promises to pose this need in the next decade. An increasing proportion of policy benefits in farming will come only as a by-product of urban social legislation.

But agriculture is likely to be well treated by society, perhaps even better than if farm groups themselves had to fashion a single policy for the future out of their conflicting interests. United States society has been extremely kind and patient with agriculture, in the amount of funds appropriated both directly and indirectly to compensate for the costs of progress and in the amount of time allowed for experimenting with different policies. Few other industries have fared as well.

The future urban society is unlikely to withdraw opportunities for compensation policies from agriculture, but it may ask how its funds are spent and whether they are in fact solving the major farm problems to which they are directed. Just as it emphasizes constitutional rights in civil liberties and equal employment opportunities for minorities, society will certainly help agriculture cover the costs and sacrifices falling on farm families as a result of progress that allows lower real costs for food and a release of resources, including a large investment in human resources, to the urban sector. Hence, the conflict among farm groups may not be a serious obstacle to future policies that are economically sensible and fair to farm people.

The urban society can and should decide on a reasonable

policy and bring it to agriculture, just as it does for other minority groups. It should listen openly to the various segments of agriculture as it does so, but it should emphasize policies that allow a continued contribution of agriculture to national economic growth and that compensate farm groups that otherwise sacrifice from this progress. In other words, it should assure positive-sum outcomes.

Eight important goals should prevail for future agricultural or rural policy. Policy should (1) further the progress of agriculture as part of the national emphasis on economic development and as a safeguard against future conditions that would cause the real price of food to become unreasonably high as domestic and world populations grow; (2) provide conditions so that commercial farmers who remain in agriculture realize an equitable gain from this progress; (3) provide economic opportunity and appropriate direct and indirect compensation for those families who must leave agriculture and rural communities because of further progress; (4) give appropriate attention to the concentration of poverty in agriculture and facilitate conditions that give equality of economic opportunity to those so suppressed; (5) establish price and income stability to counteract weather and supply responses that are unique to agriculture; (6) help upgrade the facilities and opportunities of the rural community generally, especially in its ability to provide welfare and social services and to educate and train people and feed them into the national economic stream with economic opportunities equal to those of other sectors; (7) bolster the effectiveness of the pricing system in allocating resources in agriculture and eliminate imperfections that dam up human resources and bring sacrifice in the farm sectors; (8) as part of the United States international goals and aspirations, contribute appropriately in knowledge, food, and related resources for meeting world hunger problems.

In general, these objectives have a goal of bringing earnings to resources in agriculture that are equal to the returns of resources of the same type in other sectors of the economy. But in some cases they are directed toward creating better human resources and a higher payoff from them than have come from the rural community.

These policy objectives are directed toward positive-sum outcomes for all major groups related to agriculture, including those who will remain to operate larger farms and produce more output, those who will or should leave agriculture to realize improved economic opportunities elsewhere, and other persons of rural communities who are adversely affected by structural adjustments in farming and a decline in the agricultural labor force. These farm policy goals are consistent with more generalized and widely accepted national economic goals that can be summarized as economic progress, an equitable distribution of income, and economic stability and security. These generalized goals can serve as criteria for judging any policy, but for the purposes of workable policy in agriculture, we must come down to more specific objectives.

The public should continue its investment in improvement of agriculture, especially because of the high return to society at large. The private sector will accentuate its effort in developing new capital technologies to be sold for the improvement of agriculture. Both of these forces will cause capital technologies such as fertilizer, machines, and improved seeds and feeds to replace labor further.

While more people are needed to produce machines and chemicals for agriculture and fewer to produce food, unfortunately the labor replaced from agriculture rarely has the skills for the corresponding jobs created in industry. It is important that development of agriculture continue as part of national economic growth, but our policies and economic forces should not replace labor from agriculture and then leave it stranded without opportunity in the rural community. It is important that we have policies that apply both to

those who are forced to leave agriculture and those who remain. It is also important that our policies consider the entire complex of the rural community. Policies that have the
effect of lifting income problems from farmers but of transferring an income problem to other persons in the rural community will never have economic or political acceptability.

An example of this nature was the Soil Bank and Conservation Reserve programs of the 1950's. These programs were
quite favorable to the farmers. Putting his entire farm into
the program, he could collect a cash payment and move
away. Many farmers did, and the exodus tended to concentrate in rather marginal areas of farming. They received
compensation to redress any direct or indirect income sacrifice, and land was taken out of production to lessen the
rapid accumulation of surplus stocks. However, as farmers
moved away, there were fewer customers to support local
merchants and other institutions of rural towns. A protest
soon developed and local nonfarm people were able to exert
enough pressure to ward off other programs of this type.
They preferred income compensation and production control programs that took only part of each farmer's land out
of crops, so that he stayed as a patron of local institutions.

Solution of the basic resource and adjustment problems
of agriculture will require a further exodus of people from
farms. To suppose otherwise is to evade the basic issue.
However, it is equally important that we recognize the
townspeople in the rural community as part of the agricultural complex and changing society that relates to national
economic progress and the general urbanization process,
and that we consider them when we fashion agricultural
and related policies. This does not mean that we should cut
off all programs that will solve the farm problem because
they will upset obsolete rural economic, social, and political
structures, but rather that we should extend policy so that it
provides opportunities and facilities for all people of rural
communities.

The consequences of economic growth, particular factor prices and capital technology that give rise to extended scale economies, are repeated in all important economic and social sectors of rural communities separated geographically from major growth and industrial centers. They bite deeply into these rural communities because there is not enough industrial development to absorb the labor and families released in the more general substitution of capital for human effort. Because of the scale economies that are available in all types of enterprises, including the country grocery store or the country school, and because of the thinning of farm labor force and population, the rural community must itself expand its geographic boundaries. The rural community generally in geographically dispersed farm areas has the same developmental and adjustment problems as does the individual farm. Nonfarm people stranded in rural communities, and with income losses resulting from the same variables causing depression of the farm income and labor force, are no less important than farm people. Policy should be developed accordingly.

Farm policy formulation appears to be a complex and time-consuming process. Agreement on ends and means of solving apparently obvious problems seems difficult, and the resulting policy is often anything but systematic. But permanent long-run policies seldom are developed and accepted quickly. Because democratic societies are composed of millions of persons with varying preferences or values, balance in goal attainment must be decided in the political process, with appropriate consideration for the values and needs of the many groups that make up the society. Rather than to articulate a single long-run policy and immediately adopt it, democratic societies formulate a broad general concept of long-run goals and move in this direction, away from structures existing at the moment, through a succession of short-run policies upon which agreement prevails.

This process is less spectacular and revolutionary than those political systems which force sudden breaks from the present, or which force a violent choice between alternatives, but it is more consistent with democratic procedures and positive-sum welfare outcomes. Perhaps agriculture has only recently been involved in this process. If so, it is possible that the nation can move forward more rapidly in appropriate farm policy.

PART III

POLICIES FOR
THE FUTURE

CHAPTER VI

Policies
for Those Who
Must Leave

Agricultural policy should be for all people of the industry, not just those who will remain in farming. Is not a family that must leave because of advance in the industry just as important as one who remains to have its income improved through farm programs?

To speak of the need for labor to move out of agriculture appears cold and cruel to many people. Yet agricultural policies and philosophies that focus entirely on compensation for those who remain in agriculture are cruel because they stand to limit the earning power and economic opportunity of an important stratum of the farm population. They divert attention from the many persons who are aided little or not at all by typical farm programs—support prices, commodity storage, land payments, and reduced output—and for whom opportunity is closed by fixation on such policies.

The basic, enduring, and most encompassing problem of

agriculture is that of too many resources in relation to demand arising out of the high rate of technical progress that allows more food to be produced with less labor and land. While many people have left the industry, not enough have done so to bring the returns to labor to the needed level. When the outflow of displaced workers is too slow, the backup of labor exerts tendencies toward more output, inflated land prices, lower income, and depressed returns to labor.

With continued technological change in agriculture, rapid industrial growth and full employment are the most important means to absorb labor displaced in farming and to provide greater opportunity for people who move from agriculture. When the national rate of unemployment rises to 5 percent, the opportunity for industrial employment by farm persons drops by a much greater percentage because they typically lack skills as great as those workers released from industry. This lack causes them to be among the last to find employment and the first to be laid off under unemployment. As the country recovers from recessions, the urban industrialist does not seek workers among unemployed farm people hundreds of miles away; he turns first to the city unemployed near at hand. In 1954, migration from farms fell to zero, following the small recession of 1953-1954, when national unemployment increased to only 5 percent. Migration from farms also was hampered by the slow national growth rate of the late 1950's and early 1960's.

For these reasons, it is obvious that the most important long-run program for agriculture actually is that of *fiscal* and *monetary policies* that spur the national growth rate and ward off unemployment.* People who are underemployed in agriculture then can find their way out to im-

---

* In this connection, see two other books in this series: R. L. Heilbroner and P. L. Bernstein, *A Primer on Government Spending* (New York: Random House, 1963); P. L. Bernstein, *A Primer on Money, Banking, and Gold* (New York: Random House, 1965).

proved employment opportunities. The fewer persons remaining can operate with more resources and should be able to generate more income per family. This process will occur even without various programs to aid it, but in a highly imperfect manner. Accordingly, a national environment that facilitates growth must be maintained. Fiscal and monetary policies that maintain a high national growth rate stand to bring greater gains to many people now in agriculture than to people in other industries or than any farm policy now in effect.

While economic growth and full employment is one element of an overall policy to provide an equitable deal for all people now in agriculture and the rural community, improved educational and vocational training facilities are also necessary. Youth in farm communities are at a great disadvantage, as opportunities to develop personal skills through education and vocational training are meager in rural areas in general and in low-income farm regions particularly. Farm youth, and those of the rural community at large, thus have unequal opportunities in comparison with youth from urban areas in taking advantage of future economic growth.

Several aspects of education in rural communities have led to this disadvantage. First, the method of financing education at the local level, property taxes within the local district, has crimped the rural community, because it has less property to serve as a tax base in generating funds for education. The declining rural population and local financing has led to a greater cost per taxpayer, as compared to urban locations. Selective migration has left older people in rural communities, who have a shorter planning horizon and are less inclined to make large educational investments for the future. Moreover, the net flow of educational investment from the rural community is always outward. With declining numbers and opportunities in farming and a long-standing net out-migration, rural communities have consistently invested in education of young people who end up in the urban economic sector. People do not flow into farm communities, bringing educational investment from the urban sector. The net effect of these forces is a lower quality, less inspiring, and less complete educational program in the rural community. Some rural high schools even lack courses in chemistry, biology, or mathematics beyond geometry.

While the figures are weighted somewhat heavily by the South, national data show that youth from rural communities rank much lower than urban youth in standard tests for reading, arithmetic, and other basic skills. They have a higher retardation rate (pupils one or more years behind their age group) than urban schools, and a dropout rate about twice as great as in urban communities. Less than one-third of white persons and less than 10 percent of Negroes classified as rural have finished high school, and the proportion of rural youth who attend college is much smaller than for urban youth.

In the recent past, salaries for teachers in counties where the population is 85 percent rural with 50 percent or more on farms have averaged only 55 percent of those in urban areas with 25,000 or more in population. The comparison is even much more bleak if it is made with cities having a population of 100,000 or more. Annual expenditure per pupil in the same rural areas has been less than two-thirds that of these urban areas. It is doubtful that equality in education, and hence in economic opportunity, can be provided without much more state and federal aid to education in the rural communities.

Funds provided by the Elementary and Secondary Education Act of 1965 and some of the Community Action programs of the Economic Opportunity Act of 1964 will give modest aid in upgrading rural community schools. However, in the typically dispersed commercial farming regions that do not qualify as poverty nests, these provisions are still inadequate to the unique needs of an adjusting agriculture that is reducing its work force requirements. Finances and facilities must be increased to extend and enrich the school curriculum, to provide premium teacher salaries drawing equally competent personnel into the countryside, and to initiate adequate programs of vocational training and occupational guidance.

In short, larger efforts and extended federal aid are required before facilities in rural communities can reach the level of those in urban centers and the ratio of benefit to cost is equalized between the rural community and the national society.

There has been practically no link between education in the rural community and vocational training for a nonfarm trade or skill. Farm communities have had vocational and technical education and training for boys from two sources, but both are directed toward farming and returning youths to farms. Both are financed largely by federal funds. Most high schools in rural communities have a vocational agricultural education department where participants can devote half or more of their school time learning improved farming methods. In addition, each county has a staff of extension educational experts, related to the state universities, who provide extracurricular education for youth through 4-H clubs, aimed largely at farming as a vocation. Both of these vocational programs have been exceedingly effective in teaching better farming methods, but their very success leads to fewer employment opportunities in agriculture. As some boys remain to be better farmers, many fewer farmers are needed. As these programs cause other youth to be replaced from farming, other types of vocational training are lacking. Hence, those displaced are extremely handicapped in obtaining nonfarm skills for the job market of industrial and urban sectors.

In an optimally organized educational program for geographic locations and occupations where the employment opportunities are declining, vocational training would be directed more toward feeding youth into other occupations and locations. Yet in our farm areas with the greatest pressure for migration by farm youth, the main thrust of vocational funds for boys is on agriculture, even though farm boys need a large investment toward industries and professions to put them on an equal footing with urban youth.

For example, leaving out funds allocated to home economics, Iowa spends about 70 percent on vocational agriculture, and Georgia and Mississippi about 75 percent—with the remainder for trades and industries going mainly to the large towns of the states. The West North Central region of the United States, which includes such large cities as Chicago and St. Louis, devotes about 60 percent to vocational agriculture. In contrast, New York State has only about 14 percent going to vocational agriculture and 86 percent to trades and industry. The corresponding figures are 13 and 87 percent for the New England region. Hence, in the more industrialized states, where youth already are better acquainted with occupations in industry and the professions, the greater part of vocational education is allocated to these fields of growing employment.

Rural areas have tended to be somewhat antagonistic toward federal aid to education, even though they are most in need of it and they, in fact, were the first to be given it. Training in vocational agriculture has been financed through federal funds since its very outset, through the Smith-Hughes Act in 1917, as has a large part of the 4-H training programs initiated in 1909. Rural citizens seem to overlook this facet of federal aid to education when they point with pride to their Future Farmers clubs and 4-H clubs and the vocational training they have thus attained. Without more federal aid, or state aid where possible, the quality of education in the typical rural communities will remain low. Furthermore, a distortion in the distribution of costs and benefits will prevail as citizens of areas such as western Kansas pay the costs of education while Los Angeles, San Francisco, Portland, and similar cities reap the benefit of productivity from the youth who migrate. In the typical rural counties, less than one-third of the high school graduates have remained in the community; fewer may do so in the future.

This focus of vocational training on farming has hampered the movement of people out of agriculture who are being replaced by new capital technology. It has caused favorable occupational opportunity to be closed to many people, or to be open only after they have stumbled to it after several years of considerable financial sacrifice.

As investment is made in education and research for agriculture, we need to extend services that help restore balance in the resource and income structure of the industry. We must maintain an appropriate level of research, education, and programs that aid in economic efficiency for farmers remaining in the industry. Agriculture is a competitive industry and it will continue to be so. Vocational education and a flow of information to operators who remain in farming need to be continued for economic growth purposes. Young people must be trained to take their place, and their training should be even better than in the past, considering the growing commercialization and competition of agriculture. A parallel effort is needed to educate more effectively those forced or drawn from agriculture and to aid in the structural adjustment of agriculture.

The larger adjustments in occupational and geographic migration and the activities that will facilitate them must revolve largely around the more flexible part of the farm labor force, the youth. Balance will be created as much by preventing young people from entering agriculture when their incomes and life satisfactions will be greater in some other occupation. We provide a positive service to these persons by training and counseling them so that they make correct choices when they enter the labor force. We provide them a disservice if we encourage or allow them to enter farming, only to find out four or five years later that they have made a mistake and must switch occupations. In this sense, vocational training in agriculture should be considered as part of a larger systematic vocational training program.

The Vocational Education Act of 1963 will help to bring more training to the rural community; yet it is inadequate to meet the unique needs of an adjusting agriculture in dispersed communities. It still requires the rural states, which will lose most of the skilled work force they train, to match society in investing in post-high school vocational training from which they will reap the major benefit. Its area vocational-technical schools still will not put training at the disposal of enough youth. It does not overcome the inadequacy of insufficient and misdirected vocational training in high schools where the masses of students are encountered.

Several steps are necessary to provide equality of economic opportunity over the next two decades for youth in rural communities. The geographic spread of the rural community must be extended into a functional economic area so that it can realize the scale economies or cost advantages related to current capital technology. Under this revision, school districts must be made larger and investment in education must be increased to (1) provide a higher quality of education and a more comprehensive curriculum for basic education directed toward the employment needs in the national economy over the decades ahead, (2) extend investment and redirect technical education and vocational training in high schools of rural communities so that those displaced from farming will be trained to take employment in the faster growing industries of the economy, and (3) provide an appropriate number of vocational guidance and counseling personnel, both to keep more youth in school and to direct them better into occupations consistent with the nation's economic growth and manpower needs.

Recent national legislation and appropriations directed toward increasing and improving public schools and vocation-technical training should be a gain to rural communities. Organization and implementation of these programs need to be stepped up, however. Current programs are too modest relative to needs of the rural population if this segment of society is to catch up in human resource development and employment opportunity.

Another important group of migration potential is younger persons who are already established in agriculture and have put down their roots in the community. They have become farm operators and invested in farm assets or have become year-round farm workers. Some of them need to stay, and will, as they acquire the skill and resources to become successful farmers. Others simply drifted into farming because this was the tradition in their rural community, because their only training was in this direction, and because they lacked vocational guidance and counseling to direct them otherwise. Many persons in this group find, through bitter financial experience, that the rapid technical advance and the competition of agriculture does not provide them and their families with promising economic opportunities in farming.

Theirs is a hard decision, reflected in the extremely low migration rate from farms for persons between the ages of twenty-five and forty. The decision is difficult partly because they have little aid in making it. While they have ample public services at hand to advise them on the breed of hogs to raise or the place to market their cattle, they can get little organized advice on whether they are better off to stay with farming or shift to another occupation. Nor can they get much help on which pursuit to follow if they were to transfer. Their decision also is difficult because of the costs in-

volved. In liquidating their farming assets, they lose time
and income. Then there are the costs of moving and time
with earnings foregone while they seek other employment or
look around for jobs that match any flexible skills they still
possess. Also, they are in competition with persons of the
same age bracket who grew up in industrial employment.
While the inherent abilities of a forty-year-old Kansas wheat
farmer and an electronics worker in Massachusetts may have
been equal, adaptive skills are no longer so. Even if the
Kansas wheat farmer is only getting one-third as much for
his labor, he is not likely to realize the return of the electronics worker if he shifts locations and occupations.

Potentials for transfer in this group include most of the 19
percent, 665,000 farmers, who produce only 6 percent of the
nation's farm sales. Even one-third of the 1.6 million farmers with sales over $5,000 are candidates in this group. It
would seem to be only minimum compensation for the society that has replaced these people through its investment in
improving the technology of agriculture and the process of
economic growth, to help retool them for alternative occupational engagement.

Not only should more retraining facilities be provided in
rural communities, but some type of in-school pay or unemployment compensation should be given those farm operators who wish to cease farming and participate in retraining. Without this compensation, many farmers with families
cannot take time out for adult retraining even if necessary
facilities were available. A mechanism with experience behind it is the postwar GI on-the-job training. During 1945-
1952, payments provided living costs and retraining opportunity for persons who wished to make productive transfers
of their skills and locations. Some programs for distressed
industrial or mining communities include these provisions.
We mention these to indicate again that the means do not
require any revolutionary social measures, but generally are
represented in public legislation accepted in the present or

past. The Netherlands and Sweden now have this very combination of schools and in-training pay specifically for persons leaving agriculture. It is working in a highly satisfactory manner in helping people to transfer from a bleak outlook on inadequate farms to growing opportunities in industrial employment.

The United States already has spent much more in subsidies than would be required to provide these types of retraining facilities and payments. We should break from the past and compensate people who take this step in transfer, rather than pay cash subsidies to people only if they remain in farming. In the end, the investment would pay a much higher return to society. As it is now, much of the cash payment paid as compensation to redress income depression of agriculture ends up as inflated land values. If we extend programs of recent types over another decade, this process will continue and people will have to pay a higher price or rent for land, to remain in agriculture and participate in public subsidies. However, if we use a portion of the same funds to retrain people, the total expenditure need not be greater and we will have directed more people into employment that has a high societal payoff in terms of the pricing mechanism and rewards to human resources.

The government provides outlook services for the commodities of agriculture by means of the experts attached to the state agricultural colleges and the county agricultural extension offices and numerous state and federal publications. So thorough are these services that if a sow could read she could determine her worth any morning as a resource, to be transformed into meat at Chicago, Sioux City, Denver, or Fort Worth. Outlook services and aids are even greater for a calf born in Wyoming. Public services are available to tell him whether he should become a steer and move two years hence to a slaughtering plant in California, migrate as a feeder for fattening in Iowa, or become a bull and move to

Wisconsin for more specialized employment. A farm youth's employment outlook and services do not begin to compare with these.

A large expansion is needed in services to inform farm people of nonfarm job openings and personal adjustments required for new employment and new living environments. Emphasis should be on interregional job communication and geographic transfer of farm people. The existing facilities of the state and national employment services could, if extended to a broader basis, provide another means to supplement education and training in helping agriculture adjust to economic growth. The ideal would be a national "market clearing house," similar to commodity and stock markets, to disseminate information on positions, wage rates, and skill requirements. These "market quotations" provided by the employment services could be complemented by the public's Agricultural Extension Service of the state universities, which would help carry information to farm people who may wish to migrate.

Information and service should not be restricted to the sending end of transfers, but should be extended to the receiving end as well. Migrating farm families also need help in making friends, finding housing, becoming integrated into a community, and so forth. If they are given information about the living conditions and family adjustments required, they will be able to avoid moving to communities with which their living patterns and social values are inconsistent and they will be less likely to become discouraged and return to the old community. This aid, provided by a broad and well-integrated national employment service, would not require completely new machinery. It has already been used in helping to relocate Indians from reservations to industrial employment and in facilitating migration of Puerto Rican labor to the continental United States.

Provision of these aids to scattered rural areas is costly and difficult, but it is as important as the traveling libraries

and mail service the public now provides for those who re-
side in rural communities. It is as important as the public
investment in schools and roads, which provide the basis for
people to leave, but are not fully used for these purposes
because people do not know their worth in the outside
world.

Miscellaneous other means can be used to aid those farm
workers who have innate abilities to be transferred but who
are handicapped by the geographic separation of farming
from urban industrial centers and lack skill in demand by
nonfarm sectors, or are too old to make a useful occupational transfer.

Over much of the major farming regions, industrial development does not exist and favorable nonfarm employment can be had only with a long move. Some of the funds
now going as farm subsidies could better be used to cover
transportation and relocation costs, especially for the 665,-
000 full-time units with sales under $5,000, who wish to
transfer from agriculture. Quite typically, these transfers involve movements from the Southeast to the North, or from
the Great Plains region to the West Coast.

The cost of transfer is related directly to family size, distance, and involvement in farming. Cost of moving is a
trivial capital outlay for nonfarm persons finding new employment in their own community. It is an insignificant cost
for a young person who has no commitment to others and
who looks upon the move to a new community as a venture.
But transfer costs, plus the living costs during the period of
transfer and employment location, can tax the resources of
persons with small income and no savings. In lieu of the
traditional farm subsidies, a flat subsidy to cover transportation costs for eligible persons moving out of farming would
overcome passive employment services. Or loans could be
made to cover transportation for moving and living costs
until employment is obtained. This mechanism also has

precedent. Although indentured servitude is not recommended as an acceptable mobility means, it drew a large proportion of immigrants to the United States and was in effect such a procedure. The indentured servant received his subsistence while he worked a contracted period of time to repay his prepaid transportation and upkeep costs. More typical of today's wealthy society, industrial concerns and the government pay the cost of moving when their employees are transferred from one location to another. The payment or loan would seem equally logical to aid the mobility of farm families who are displaced by farm technological advance fostered by society.

Persons of fifty-five years or older whose skills and cultural orientations are almost inflexibly tied to agriculture have few opportunities to move to nonfarm occupations. Experience in milking cows is of little value in assembling electronic components or handling printouts from a computer. Their age alone puts them at a disadvantage in securing nonfarm employment. And because shifting from farming often means moving several hundred miles and living in a different type of community, few of them want to move. Generally, their personal future is best in agriculture.

For these older farm persons who lack flexibility in skills and have no prospect of retraining and relocation, current subsidies, paid if they remain in farming, might be reversed. They would then be given payments if they terminated farming operations. United States society has precedent in providing severance payment to those released from particular employment. Such pay is traditional for armed services as well as many private firms. Its equivalent for technological unemployment or replacement in industry also is provided in unemployment compensation, possible between jobs, under the Social Security Act. Use of this principle, as capital investment to increase labor mobility, or as compensation reflecting recognition of a degree of technological unemployment opportunity and labor demand, might well have aided many persons to transfer, lowering total costs of programs and adding to the welfare of selected persons.

Thus severance payments might be used effectively with two groups of people: (1) Those who are still young enough for retraining and employment in other industries. In this case, the severance payment might be a substitute for, or be meshed with, transportation and retraining payments. Individuals could choose between remaining in agriculture and receiving the existing small annual payments or leaving agriculture and receiving immediately in lump-sum form the amount that would otherwise accrue to them in the next several years. (2) Those who are too old to transfer and otherwise remain underemployed at low income in agriculture. For them, severance pay could take the form of social security payments started at an earlier age. For example, if they ceased farming, their social security payments might be started at age fifty-five. Persons starting at fifty-five would have a lower payment, with the rate scaled up by years to sixty-five. Hence, all would eventually graduate from the program. The Netherlands is using this plan for retiring older farmers so that their small resource holdings can be recombined into adequate-sized units by farmers who remain. This kind of program could be on a voluntary basis so that only those who deem themselves to be made better off would participate.

The policy elements outlined above, plus those programs proposed by the Office of Economic Opportunity, are best able to handle the poverty problem concentrated in farming. Largely, the programs of the Office of Economic Opportunity are directed to the city poor, although the density of the problem is greater in agriculture. The programs do have some elements aimed directly at the farm poor, but these are too few and some are in the wrong direction. They are based on obsolete agrarian fundamentalism. Along with a few minor steps, the major component of the program for farmers is to provide more capital—up to $5,000—to low-income farmers and keep them in the industry. But there is not room for all of these families at favorable income levels in agriculture, and even if low-income families could earn 10 percent on the $5,000, which most of them cannot in the absence of large managerial aids, it would still not push their income up to levels of decency in today's affluent society.

Some of them simply must leave, so that their meager resources can be gathered together and consolidated into viable economic units for those who remain. This requires not $5,000 but a minimum of $30,000; in many cases, it means $50,000 for those who remain. The steps to solve the poverty problem in agriculture must be much bolder. The programs outlined in this chapter are more appropriate for the great number who have more income to gain in retraining and occupational migration.

The economic and social problems of farm and nonfarm people in rural communities cannot be separated. Both groups are faced with adjustments stemming from the rapid inflow of new technology into agriculture and the subsequent replacement of labor and the reduction in farm numbers.

Indeed, the same scale economies in operation on farms also affect other rural businesses and institutions. The structure of the rural community has long been obsolete, and it is becoming more so as automation and other technical developments cause machinery and facilities to replace labor. Farm communities are almost as overequipped with towns as they are with farm labor. On the average, income of nonfarm persons in communities lacking industrial activity is little better than that of agriculture.

Hence, some minimum compensation perhaps needs to be provided for the nonfarm population in rural communities required to make large-scale shifts in land use, farm size, and farm population. This minimum compensation might include, as well as the retraining and relocation or severance compensation mentioned above for the farm population, such measures as (1) an extended or ten-year averaging of income tax payments, (2) federal aid to education designed specifically for these regions and to offset reductions in the property tax base, (3) special college scholarships for eligible youth, and (4) some means for compensation of losses in asset values in rural towns as the farm population thins even more. Increase in economic opportunities to strengthen and aid the rural community, as it adjusts further to technological change in agriculture and national economic growth, must be given priority equal to that of compensation and aid for strengthening the agricultural economy.

If economic development took place evenly over the country, it would provide a painless means to alleviate the problems of the rural community. It would provide jobs on the spot for the excess labor born in rural communities which has always had to migrate. In contrast to the typical geographic migration necessary for labor replaced from industrially remote farm areas, it would not involve large moving costs, the task of settling into a new home, and adjustments to new customs and neighborhoods. More farm families could become part-time farmers, taking on a non-farm job but continuing to operate their crops and livestock.

Almost every country town and farm community hopes that it can solve its problems by local industrial development. It is a fact, however, that not every community can be a developing one, paralleling the rate of growth in the national economy.* Unfortunately, some economic regions will always spurt ahead of national economic growth, while

---

* Solution of problems in technological change and employment problems would actually require a greater rate of growth for farm communities than for the nation, given the rate of change in farm technology and the net migration from agriculture.

others lag behind and become declining communities. Farm regions are replete with villages where the population is decreasing and the store buildings and dwellings are rapidly declining in capital value. This is a double dose of bitter medicine: an erosion in one's life capital as real estate values dwindle from a thinning of business volume, at a time when the national economy is bounding forward.

Some rural communities do have opportunities in industrial development. They must be favored in location and transportation facilities, possess some new or undeveloped resource that takes on a higher marginal urgency with national economic growth, or have a high quality labor force and be near population centers. Unfortunately, however, the very nature of farm communities, dispersed over the plains or vast grazing areas, means that those with central problems of adjustment frequently do not have the requisite conditions and resources. The core of the farm country is far away from large cities, thus causing transportation costs to limit industrial development.

For much of agriculture that still has adjustments in farm numbers and the work force, there is no promise of solutions by developing industry in the county-seat town. Efforts that lead communities without opportunity to false hopes in these respects cause frustration and dissipation of human resources. People are encouraged to remain under the expectation that the community can eventually generate industry, only to find that they must make a move under more agonizing conditions a few years later.

Even where the necessary conditions and resources are present, industrialization will not obviate the adjustment of farm numbers and sizes to technological change and national economic development. It can, however, provide the overall community with greater economic opportunities. In rural areas, the new jobs created usually draw largely on housewives who were formerly teachers or clerical workers,

newly graduated high school students, filling station operators, and other technicians from neighboring communities.
A small proportion is represented by replaced farmers.
Though not always providing large alternative employment
to farmers, industrialization can add to local business and
development even in this case. In other cases, replaced farmers and local businessmen can be fitted into the new network. In general, however, adequate retraining facilities
could allow more locally displaced persons to have the benefits of industrial development within the community.

The public has invested some funds aimed fairly directly
at solution of low farm incomes by industrial development.
The Rural Development program of the 1950's focused
mainly on farmers in attempting to provide facilities for
more education and vocational training, encourage farm en-
largement and increased part-time farming, and facilitate
a fuller utilization of underemployed farm labor in defense
industries. Like many new programs, it hardly got off the
ground when this new administration changed the name to
the Rural Areas Development program in the early 1960's
and emphasized, along with the above mix of goals, broader
objectives. These included expansion of job opportunities
by stimulating investment in all types of services and manu-
facturing, development of recreational opportunities in
local areas, and investing further in protection and management of natural resources and wild life. Various other programs were added in the 1960's, which emphasized depressed areas such as the West Virginia mining region:
programs in vocational training at the community level
under the Manpower Development and Training program
of the Departments of Labor and Health, Education and
Welfare, and the Accelerated Public Works programs under
the Department of Commerce. The latter had the purpose
of providing immediate work to the unemployed and underemployed through such public works as roads, flood con-

trol, sewer systems, and camp sites and by encouraging commercial industrialization and investment of various kinds.
The antipoverty programs of the Office of Economic Opportunity provide similar orientations through its youth programs, urban and rural Community Action programs, assistance to small businesses, vocational training and work
experience for heads of low-income families, and other special programs to combat poverty.

While it sometimes has been difficult to define the problems of individual communities and to devise a mode of
operation for them, these programs have been in the right
direction especially for creating economic opportunity for
distressed areas and families in poverty. Since even commercial farming areas are distressed to an extent, more of the
programs relating to retraining and industrial development
should be extended to them. Erasing the concentration of
that portion of the nation's poverty which is concentrated in
agriculture itself merits vigorous national effort and a special program mix.

However, solution of the poverty problem of agriculture
will not also solve the problems of commercial agriculture in
widespread communities where the major task is adjustment
to technological change, larger farms, and a smaller population. Many, probably the majority, of these communities are
not located or endowed in a manner allowing industrial development to help them. Neither are they located amidst
mountains and lakes so that land representing excess production capacity can be shifted to recreational purposes and
draw in tourists and associated employment opportunities
and require large-scale construction work for roads, parks,
camp sites, and motels.

The answer still is improved education and vocational
training to feed better equipped young people into the national labor force and to provide retraining and other personal investments for those who must shift from farms and

stores over the rural countryside. This needs to be the emphasis, along with the other possibilities in compensation, for the majority of the rural commercial farm communities. Of course, wherever possible and economically favorable, communities with the proper endowment should be aided in economic development.

For those communities where further thinning of the population is in sight and that do not qualify as strictly distressed poverty areas, the geographic spread of the community must be extended so that it provides a viable economic and civil unit. The typical rural county was laid out more than a hundred years ago in the time of horse travel and a lower stage of capital technology. Today this unit is too small and has too few persons to be efficient in economic functions such as retailing and recreation, public services such as schools and churches, and civil services such as local government. To allow a sufficient supply and low cost of services, existing counties and trading areas will have to be combined into much larger units.

The rural community just cannot support as many towns as in the past. Social and welfare services and recreational opportunity already are in small supply. Medical services are much more scant than in cities. Rural communities have roughly only one-third as many physicians, surgeons, and dentists per 1,000 of population as do cities; they have only one-half as many nurses. Not only are schools, roads, public utilities, and civil services often inadequate, but they come at a high cost because of the sparse population and tax base. Without reorganization of rural communities and their facilities, the cost per capita will continue to grow rapidly with further reductions in farms. Rural residents will fall further behind their city cousins in the welfare, social, and public services that affluent citizens demand. Some experts estimate that if these disparities are overcome, the number of country towns must decrease proportionately more than the number of farms; that a town as a shopping center in each fifty miles is most consistent with today's technology over much of the farm territory; and that efficient public services at a reasonable cost can be provided with only one-fifth or one-tenth as many counties and county seats as now exist.

Changes of this magnitude involve large costs and complex adjustments. As part of the minimum compensation to rural communities, society needs to provide them with the research and planning aids for reconstituting their communities and commercial and public services. There are many alternatives for regrouping, with savings in some directions offsetting greater costs in other directions. With fewer farms, we may need a surfaced road for each four square miles rather than for every square mile as at the present. Reduction in the number of county governments would contribute similarly. These accomplishments are necessary, as a social policy extending beyond pockets of rural poverty under programs of the Office of Economic Opportunity, if a Great Society is truly to be attained. Initiation of appropriate rural community policies only awaits the imagination to initiate them—and the political acceptance of those in control of rural communities who frequently resist them. While it may seem cruel to help plan the abandonment of scattered rural villages, it is even more cruel to let them simply rot away with decaying opportunity for their youth—as is now the case.

These are the programs and policies aimed at people—the people who sacrifice most from agricultural change. Farm policies to date have largely focused on land, in controlling it as an input, and grain storage. Hence, they have been aimed at the people of farming and rural communities who suffer least from agricultural change. A main long-run result of ongoing policies is that of higher land values, so that the income increment is cancelled for the next generation of farmers. What we need is a program that has the main long-run effect of broadening economic opportunity for the masses of the rural community. Some of the large funds now used for current farm programs must be shifted to these purposes.

CHAPTER VII

Policies
for Those Who
Will Stay

Come what may, we are going to use a smaller and smaller proportion of the nation's resources in agriculture. Food will, of course, remain a necessary ingredient of life. But, for a people who have enough of it and who worry more about obesity than about something to eat, it will take on greatest marginal urgency as a medium around which entertainment, business deals, and absorption of the individual's time revolves. For the typical person, it will approach the utility level of water and air. Frantic suffering would occur with too little and death would result from none, but well-fed people will hardly give it a second thought. Their motivations will stem not from need for food, but from the desire to have more elaborate automobiles, air conditioning, color TV, education, travel, recreation, and other accessories of affluent consumers—or, in a different way, to improve the quality of life in the sprawling urban and industrial centers.

Nevertheless, farmers and food producers will still be necessary, and commercial farmers who remain to produce food will still be faced with the special problems of the farming industry. Continued national economic development and farm technological improvement, affecting the prices, productivity, and substitutability of capital, labor, and land resources, will bring further structural adjustments in farming. The ability to produce in surplus amounts will still prevail over the next decade for individual commodities, and probably, depending on international policies in food aid to underdeveloped countries, for food in aggregate.

The pure-competition characteristics of farming also will prevail, unless their market effects are offset by policy organized by government or farm organizations. Instability of output and prices, unless offset through policy, will continue as a result of vagaries in weather or producer response to prices. Agricultural policy directed at commercial farmers should focus on alleviation of problems that stem from these circumstances.

The number of farms and the labor force of agriculture will decrease significantly in the years to come. As the number declines, those farmers who remain are likely to have greater managerial abilities and more education than those leaving. They will tend to use more capital and produce more from the same land. Consequently, the projected reduction in the farm labor force will not curtail the nation's ability to produce food in the future, any more than it has in the past. That these trends are in prospect is emphasized by the fact that the average age of United States farmers is now more than fifty years and nearly one-third are over fifty-five. Aided by those leaving agriculture for employment elsewhere, retirements over the next fifteen years will result in a turnover of the majority of farm managers. Further transformation of agriculture will be accelerated accordingly.

About 900,000 farms out of a total of 3.5 million now produce three-fourths of the nation's farm sales, but 750,000 farms could well do the job by 1980 (although some projections indicate that as few as 500,000 farms could easily provide food for us in 1980). A like number of part-time and semiretirement units would bring the total down to 1.5 million farms, or less than one-half the present level. With this decline in numbers, the size of commercial farms will more than double. The labor force of agriculture will drop to as low as 3 million active workers, as farms increase in size and become more specialized. Hence, 4 percent or less of the nation's labor force will be engaged in food production.

Other inputs and resources will change accordingly. The industry will make only modest increases in its total real estate capital, land and buildings, because there will be fewer units operating the given land supply. Total real estate capital for the farm industry is expected to grow only 5 to 10 percent by 1980. However, due to smaller numbers, real estate capital per commercial farm will more than double. More total capital from nonfarm sources—fertilizer, chemicals, machinery, petroleum—will be used. Agriculture in total will employ around 75 percent more of these inputs, but the per farm use of these capital items will approximately triple.

Obviously, there are great capital problems ahead for the individual farm. While the industry will make only modest increases in total capital inputs, the individual farm will make large increases. The industry will halve its labor force, but individual farms will hold their labor force constant or increase it slightly. More units will be two-man farms, manned by the operator and a year-round hired man and less help from the housewife and children. There will also be a large increase in highly specialized units, especially in livestock units that hire several workers and raise 50,000-100,000 broilers, feed 10,000-20,000 herd of cattle or milk 1,000-2,000 cows.

The above projections for resource structure and inputs are based on an increase in food output by 1980 of 50 percent over 1960. This increase can come with ease, requiring only a 10 percent aggregate increase in inputs when the decline in labor is balanced against the increase in capital for the industry as a whole. If foreign requirements or other unforeseen circumstances cause demand to increase by more than 50 percent, the increment in resource inputs will need to be greater than 10 percent. American farm industry has considerable capacity yet to be tapped, and the extent to which surplus-producing potential remains to plague commercial farms depends on domestic agricultural policies, international policy and market conditions affecting commercial exports of farm products, and the extent of the nation's future commitments in feeding mushrooming populations of less developed countries.

The nation's capacity to produce surplus food would vanish overnight if we suddenly decided to donate food to all overpopulated countries. However, it appears unlikely that the United States will be called upon to unleash each bit of its farm supply potential in the next decade.

One major problem in this respect will be that of releasing capacity at a rate that is realistic in terms of growing world demand for food and further increases in the nation's farm production potential. The nation has had 60 million acres of cropland demobilized from production under various supply control programs initiated in the late 1950's and early 1960's. The important question now is, How fast will foreign demand or international food aid expand to absorb the production potential represented by this land?

The question hinges around exports because growth in domestic demand will not increase as fast as technological improvement and the supply ability of American agriculture. The projections of a 50 percent greater output by 1980, through an increase of 10 percent in aggregate inputs, suppose a 100 percent increase in exports plus a 42 percent increase in domestic demand due to population and per capita income increases. With only a 50 percent increase in total food demand and production, food-producing ability would still increase more rapidly than demand to 1980, if technological trends of the last two decades were continued into the future. Under this condition the acreage demobilized from production in 1966 would need to grow to 80 million by 1980 if the real price of farm products were to be maintained.

It is apparent that world food demand and requirements will cause United States farm exports to more than double in the next fifteen years, so that surplus acreage, in the above context, will not increase by another third in the next fifteen years. Yet it also is apparent that the United States has large production potential and some sort of supply balancing will be needed for some time if farm price levels are to be maintained or international food aid grows only gradually. Hence, we come to the question of how this control should be exercised, if indeed it should.

To offset its investment in the development and supply capacity of agriculture, the American public has used various types of direct and indirect compensation policies to maintain or increase farm income; direct compensation represented by payments to farmers for withdrawing land from production, and by a few other payment forms and indirect compensation represented by government storage programs, foreign surplus disposal, and production controls that lessen domestic marketings and output thus bolstering prices and farm incomes. Evidently, use of the two major sets of policies together, development and compensation, has general public acceptance as a means of assuring positive-sum outcomes from technological improvement in agriculture. Together they allow some decline in the real price of food for consumers but prevent, because of the inelastic demand for food, a steep decline in farm income. The principle of compensation has acceptance in economic theory and practice, and the fact that American society has been willing to finance it for several decades indicates that it also has public acceptance.

Hence, it may be unnecessary to question the need or logic of compensation. But we are justified in evaluating the methods used. A wide range of possibilities exist.

Are indirect methods—storing surplus stocks, paying farmers for holding land out of production, and shipping surpluses abroad—the most efficient means? Numerous direct compensation methods would be cheaper; they could lessen the cost and administrative difficulties of farm programs. One is direct cash payments made purely for income compensation purposes and without relation to production control. By various criteria, the compensation due each farmer must be calculated as a lump-sum amount and a check mailed to him. Each farmer would produce the amount consistent with his resources and the price structure of the free market. With the market cleared through the forces of supply and demand, the public would not need to acquire and carry large stocks to support prices and bolster farm income, (though it might still acquire stocks needed to bring stability to market prices and food aid). Compensation, mailed directly from the Treasury, would represent the difference between farm income determined by market forces and the income level deemed consistent with economic progress and equity.

Because lump-sum compensation would not enter into the cost or return of products or be paid in proportion to production, it should have little effect on output, and supply would tend to level out at the market equilibrium level.

Lump-sum compensation is in contrast to a subsidy tied to the amount of commodity produced. Per unit subsidy has been the main postwar policy instrument in Great Britain; it guarantees low-cost food to the consumer and provides favorable farm income. Paid from the Exchequer, part of the cost of food for the low-income family is thus born by the high-income taxpayer. This method is used in the United States for wool and sugar. The farmer markets his product for whatever it will bring in the market, then is paid through the Treasury for the difference between the market price and the level deemed to be a parity or equitable price.

The major limitation of this method is that it places a great premium on increasing output and can result in an overage of resources in agriculture, the production of too much food relative to other goods and services. In less developed countries where the supply problem is too little food, the price subsidy can be an effective instrument for increasing output and upgrading diets. But where the supply problem is that of too much food, the per unit subsidy only adds fuel to the fire. It is also the most costly of all Treasury subsidy forms. It brings greater output, thus causing prices to decline and more subsidy to be required for each unit produced.

A lump-sum subsidy largely is divorced from this effect in producer response. While it may slightly retard the rate at which resources leave agriculture because it supplements income from the markets, it also can aid persons to transfer from farming. Paid annually only if the farmer stays in agriculture, it causes surplus resources to remain in farming when economic progress and consumer preference beckon them to other industries. However, if paid regardless of whether the farmer stays in agriculture, or all in one year rather than over a sequence of years, it will not affect marginal accounting; it should have little effect in causing surplus agricultural resources and could even provide the capital for migration.

There are other advantages of lump-sum compensation.

Tied to the individual, it would not be capitalized into asset values, soon to have its income-increasing effects cancelled. Under the present system, farmers are paid according to the number of acres they withdraw from production. This payment, plus the higher return from the remaining acres as crop prices are increased, is attached directly to the land. It therefore serves to increase the price of land. While the increment in land values serves as a capital gain to this generation of farmers, it serves as higher costs to the beginning farmer.

If agriculture is to be provided income transfers through direct compensation, lump-sum cash payments are most efficient in terms of (1) the Treasury cost of attaining a given level of compensation, (2) minimum interference with the market mechanism and the corresponding resource allocation, and (3) ease in administration. However, this method of compensation has never been favored by American farm organizations. A form of direct subsidies (on a per unit basis) was proposed for major commodities by Secretary Brannan during the Truman administration. The American Farm Bureau attacked him with vigor and ferocity and the system has not been seriously proposed since.

The resistance of some farm organizations to the lump-sum method is not entirely clear, since this method does not interfere with freedom of production decisions and could lessen society costs of a given income subsidy or transfer to farmers. Two major reasons are sometimes proposed: (1) Direct Treasury payments are more noticeable to the general public than the same amount paid by consumers through market prices when supply is lessened to conform with an inelastic demand. (2) Perhaps a "work ethic" or value held by farmers is that one should earn his income— payments from the Treasury too clearly being "public handouts." Production control, to restrain output and raise prices sufficiently to boost farm income, evidently is considered more nearly to be "earning one's salt" than direct

Treasury payments. Since nonfarm firms are able to set prices and adjust output so as to maximize their short-run income, many farmers believe that they should also use this income-boosting method as a means of attaining bargaining power and economic equality in the market.

Still, direct payments seem to be acceptable to wool and sugar farmers. In the case of wool payments, the parity price is announced in the spring. The producer sells his wool at the market price, which is lower than the parity price, and then receives a government payment making up the difference. The program is even bigger for sugar, the one output that is completely managed by the federal government. Each December the Secretary of Agriculture announces the United States sugar requirements for the next year. Quotas are then assigned both domestic and foreign producers. A tax of 50¢ per hundredweight, finally paid by the consumer, is collected by the Treasury and dispensed to American producers. In the case of wool, the public pays the subsidy in proportion to their income; in the case of sugar, in proportion to their consumption. Wool and sugar subsidies are paid to protect farmers from foreign competition, since we are net importers of both products. Other production control programs are designed to protect United States farmers against their own overproduction. This difference may help to explain why direct subsidies are accepted in the one case and not the other.

It is possible that if commercial farmers were fully informed of the alternatives and efficiency of compensation methods, they might eventually select direct payments over the more costly conventional policies in use. The public is now accustomed to large Treasury outlays for agriculture. Checks from the Treasury have been used in recent years to "hire" farmers to retire land from production. Having accepted the method for output control and price improvement, perhaps people will eventually accept it as the means of compensation, with output left free to attain levels of market equilibrium.

Direct cash compensation would be financed through the Treasury. The cost of the program falls on the public in the general pattern of federal taxation, largely in a manner progressive with income. The major format of programs to increase farm prices and income, however, has been through production controls (but also with large Treasury payments). The expectation is, since demand for food is inelastic, that the smaller output sold at a higher price will bring a greater total market revenue. While the tax system is progressive, this system of indirect compensation of farmers is regressive to income of consumers. Persons with low incomes use a greater proportion of income for food purchases and bear a heavier burden, relative to income, of the increase in farm return than persons with high incomes.

Several production or supply control methods, either voluntary or compulsory, have been used or proposed for agriculture. Voluntary control allows the individual to participate or not as he chooses. Successful voluntary control programs, if they actually reduce output and raise prices and incomes, require Treasury payments to farmers who participate. The major control programs in effect over the last decade have been voluntary with payments for participation. Farmers have not been regimented but have selected to participate when their incomes could be increased.

Compulsory control requires, through public legislation and the power of the courts, that the farmer limit his production. Compulsory control, requiring a referendum and acceptance by a majority of producers, has been used for a few products over the last two decades. Thus it has been applied over most of the nation for fluid milk through a device called marketing orders, or setting an upper quota to be marketed by each producer. For crops, it has been mainly applied continuously to a few specialized fruits and vegetables. But it has never received acceptance for other major products such as corn, hogs, rice, tobacco, and beef. A 1963 referendum proposing mandatory quotas on wheat was defeated at the polls by farmers as was an earlier vote on marketing quotas for broilers.

However, if compensation is to be provided farmers through the indirect method of reduced output and higher prices, the total public costs of obtaining a given increment in farm income will be less through compulsory quotas than through voluntary output reduction induced by payments to the farmer for participation. For example, suppose that a 10 percent reduction in output is required to increase prices by 20 percent under an inelastic demand. Production must be decreased by the same amount whether by one method or the other. Under voluntary control, farmers must be paid to reduce output. Thus the general public is faced with two increases in expenditures: one as taxpayers through the Treasury to pay farmers for reducing output and one as consumers through the market in a greater outlay for food. In the case of compulsory quotas, with each farmer required by law to reduce output without payments, the general public only pays a greater outlay for food in the market, as price rises from reduced production.

Supply control through quotas also could have other advantages as compared to voluntary control by payments. Because under the voluntary system payments are attached to the land, and thus become capitalized into land values, quotas can be attached to the individual and thus better related to human resources. In this form, we can make them negotiable so that one farmer who wants to cut back his production or pull out of farming altogether can sell them to another farmer who is expansion-minded. They can even help some persons migrate from farms with the proceeds from the quota used for the costs of transferring. However, the job of policing output or market quotas would be extremely difficult for commodities such as feed grains.

Compulsory controls have been opposed violently by the American Farm Bureau and other major farm groups. Farmers in general have too little community of interest to vote compulsory quotas upon themselves for commodities such as feed grains that stretch over the entire nation. Few rumblings of lack of freedom are heard from the commercial farmers who use these quotas in the major milk sheds or for the specialized fruits and vegetables in California. Perhaps these producers look upon themselves as having the same freedom as oil producers who operate under quotas to stabilize output and prices, or the few large firms in most major industries who do not compete on a price basis in the short run. Yet lack of freedom in production decisions is given as the reason for farmer resistance to compulsory supply controls or quotas.

More likely, however, the basic issue is one of the distribution of gains and losses from quotas or compulsory controls among farmers. They are accepted best where the product is produced in a small geographic or climatically favored area and the producers are few in number and have great homogeneity of interests. They function best here because of a single buyer of the product and because farmers cannot peddle their surplus to neighbors. The quotas, if they are successful, will raise total farm income by a specified amount through higher prices. How much of this increased income will go to farmers at different locations, representing various economic groups or producing different commodities? The size of the quota allocated each farmer will determine the share he gets. Quotas can even bring losses to some farmers. Those who oppose compulsory quotas may obtain a much larger share of the income determined in the market. Large farmers with capital to increase output may oppose them; small farmers without funds for expansion may favor them. Farmers who buy grain to produce livestock may oppose them for feeds but favor them for milk.

While there are other means for compensating farmers for income losses resulting from rapid progress in agriculture, control of production has been the accepted policy instrument in the United States for the last thirty-five years. Perhaps it will continue so unless the voting majority of non-farmers takes things into its own hands at the polls and compensates commercial agriculture in the least-cost manner, or even drops all compensation programs. Until that time, however, policies to maintain or improve farm income evidently will hinge on production control or supply reduction.

Under these prospects, should supply control be by compulsory or voluntary means? The answer depends on whether the public is willing to compensate agriculture only through the market (compulsory control) or through both the market and the Treasury (voluntary control). It also depends on whether concern with providing positive-sum welfare outcomes relates to the broader community represented by consumers and farm producers, or only to the smaller community represented by farmers. In the latter case, which thus far seems to have been the main criterion in public selection among farm program alternatives, the voluntary system has some advantages over a compulsory system. As mentioned frequently, the major basis for agricultural policy directed to commercial farmers is compensation to guarantee a positive-sum outcome for society from farm technical advance. Without compensation, consumers have a positive outcome from resource releases and lower food prices; farmers have a negative outcome from lower income. But if sufficient compensation is paid farmers, their outcome also is positive.

For the same logical reasons, we should insure that the

effects within farm policy also are positive-sum for all major farmer groups. If one group gains and another sacrifices as a result of the policy, there is no guarantee of a positive overall outcome. Voluntary programs, with payments to farmers who are willing to reduce output, more nearly guarantee positive-sum outcomes among farm groups than does compulsory control. The individual has complete freedom to accept or reject compensation. Those who accept it will do so because they anticipate a positive outcome. Those who refrain from participation have judged that their present situation is positive. Summing these positives, the overall effect should be positive and income and welfare of the farm community must be enhanced. This fact, plus the willingness of society to provide funds through the Treasury, has made voluntary programs more popular than compulsory ones.

Compulsory programs, which force output restrictions on all producers, must make quantitative judgments of the distribution of gains and losses among all individuals. (This also would be true if the free market were used to squeeze some resources out of agriculture.) Questions of distribution concern not only income, but also capital or asset values. In the United States, assignment of quotas has a direct bearing on the values of land. Some farmers realize large capital gains, others have small gains, and some may even have capital losses as a result of the distribution of the quotas used for output control. To require that all farmers reduce output by a given percentage also supposes knowledge of their cost structure and that revenue from higher prices will be increased more than costs in all cases. However, farmers with high fixed monetary costs will be at a relative disadvantage as compared to those whose fixed costs are mostly those of unpaid family resources. This difference undoubtedly gives rise to some of the conflict over compulsory supply programs, although ideological conflict and zero-sum economic competitions (what one gains the other supposedly loses from a particular type of policy) among rival farm organizations also are involved.

These aspects of choice and welfare outcomes would favor voluntary supply control programs over compulsory ones.

Not only has the nation used voluntary supply management as the main instrument to redress income sacrifices from rapid technological improvement and depressed prices for farm products, but it also has used various methods of attaining this end.

The goal of supply control programs has been to reduce output of farm products. However, the actual emphasis of supply control has not been on output as such but rather on the resources or inputs used to produce the output. Because the farmer is compensated for reducing output to a specified level, he must be policed to prevent his exceeding the quota. This task is difficult except where the commodity is perishable and there is a single buyer. The farmer can sell his product near his home or truck it to a distant market. He can market in the daytime, or start a long journey at night when watchers are in bed. He can sell it to his neighbor who is not under a quota, who can then push it into the market. If he produces corn, wheat, barley, or similar crops, he can market up to his quota and then use additional output to produce livestock on his farm, the result being the same as if he sold his grain.* Because these and other methods would be used by farmers under a supply control program, supply control has had to focus on inputs rather than outputs.

Three major categories of inputs or resources are used to produce output in agriculture. Labor is the one in greatest surplus, but agricultural policy has never tried to reduce labor input. The fact that there is a surplus of labor, with

---

* The situation has been somewhat different for farmers operating under market quotas for perishable fruits, vegetables, and milk where they sell to only one buyer near at hand.

much of it underemployed, leads to the obvious conclusion: reducing labor input up to an extent would have no effect on output. Furthermore, control of labor input would be difficult. Farmers might slip out at night and work in the fields or simply work harder and make up for fewer hours. Control on capital inputs would be equally difficult. It comes in too many forms: money, seeds, animals, tractors, binder string. Measuring it and ascertaining its reduction would be nearly impossible.

For these reasons, control of inputs has rested on the land resource. Each farm has a definite amount of land, which can be measured and remains in one spot. The production season is long and inspectors can easily ascertain whether the farmer has actually left the land out of production. Hence, from the very outset of massive compensation for agriculture, American policy has been oriented around land, withdrawing it from production or shifting it to crops and uses that are not in surplus supply.

Land can be operated only with labor and capital. Hence, it might appear that if land is withdrawn from production, the capital and labor inputs used with it also will be idled. However, this rarely happens. If the farmer with 160 acres of cropland takes 40 acres out of production, under a contract whereby he obtains $20 per acre, it may appear that he will reduce his output by one-fourth for $800. This would be true perhaps if he also left 25 percent of his labor and capital idle. Typically, however, he withdraws the 40 acres from crops but transfers the corresponding labor and capital to the remaining 120 acres. Using more fertilizer, improved seed, and other new technology, part of the anticipated reduction from the 40 acres is offset by greater output from the remaining land. Farmers often have more than made up for the reduced acreage by improved technology and greater inputs on the remaining land. They are strongly encouraged in this substitution: Higher prices brought about by lessened output on idled land causes use of more resources to be profitable on the remaining acreage. The payment for idling a fraction of the land also provides capital to purchase more inputs and the certainty of prices encourages greater use of capital. Farmers usually idle their poorest land and keep the best productive. The first increment of land withdrawn makes a small marginal contribution to supply control, the next increment more, and so on. Thus, more than 20 percent in acreage must be reduced for a 20 percent reduction in output.

Regardless of these complexities, production control based on the land input has been the foundation of agricultural policy—the complexities here are fewer than in controlling output or labor and capital inputs. Participating farmers gain from two sources: from the direct cash payment for participation and the higher market prices forthcoming as output in aggregate is reduced. Farmers who do not participate can produce the same amount or more and gain from the higher prices. The system also lends itself to political logrolling and horse trading. Feed grains, wheat, and livestock can be produced over the entire nation. Congressmen in the South may agree to support a policy to reduce cotton acreage if their constituents can replace it with corn. Congressmen from the Plains states agree for a reduction in wheat if their farmers can substitute corn or grain sorghums for it. Congressmen from the Corn Belt may agree to reduce corn acreage if soybeans or grass can be put on the land. Little wonder, then, that this horse trading allows program goals of supply reduction to be largely or fully negated—especially on feed grains, which can be produced over the entire nation. Only after 1960 was acreage reduced enough to offset these loopholes, plus normal trends in farming improvement, and make a sustained and noticeable reduction in output of major commodities.

Even under voluntary control programs centering on land, several different methods with differing impacts on resource use and rural communities can be used. These differences explain why some have been favored over others even though they do not minimize Treasury costs.

Since the initiation of national supply control programs in 1933, main reliance has been on having millions of farmers throughout the nation withdraw a fraction of their land from production. This system draws land from regions with both good and poor land. As a result, surplus land is neither withdrawn from production in a concentrated region, where it has least advantage in production, nor idled permanently. It is withdrawn as a small parcel on each participating farm. Since the farmer remains on his farm with underemployed labor and machinery, it awaits the termination of the program when it will immediately be put back into production.

Partial retirement has other disadvantages. It is more costly than whole farm retirement of land because it takes land out of production on both the most fertile and least fertile farms. Under most conditions, the cost per unit of reduced output is least if it comes from less productive soils. Since fixed costs of machinery, seed, and labor are similar, total per acre costs of production ordinarily are not proportioned to yield. Poor land that yields 40 bushels of corn per acre may have production costs of $20 per acre; fertile land that yields 100 bushels may have costs of only $30. If corn price is $1.10 per bushel, the farmer with poor land will generally remove it from production if the payment per acre for doing so is equal to or greater than the net return per acre. With a gross return of $44 (40 bushels × $1.10) and costs of $20, net return per acre is $24. Hence, with a payment of approximately $24, we would expect him to join the program and idle his land. For a payment of $24, output is reduced by 40 bushels; the cost of reduction is $24 ÷ 40 = 60¢ per bushel. On the fertile land, however, the net return is $80. Hence, to obtain a reduction of 100 bushels, we must pay a cost of $80 ÷ 100 = 80¢ per bushel of reduction.

Whole-farm retirement comes at a lower cost since it allows the farmer to close down his entire unit and cease certain fixed costs. Studies of the effects of partial retirement and whole-farm methods of land retirement suggest the former to cost about 25 percent more than the latter in attaining a given amount of long-run output reduction.

When land is retired on a whole-farm basis, the farmer cannot make up for the acreage reduction by transferring freed labor and capital to other land. This method has the cost advantage mentioned above. It lowers program costs somewhat because all farm costs, except taxes and similar outlays, can be terminated on the whole-farm basis. While it alone does not cause concentration of land retired in the least productive areas, it allows the least productive farms in all regions to be withdrawn, lowering program costs below that of the partial method and allowing more labor to be withdrawn from production. The individual need not stay on his farm to realize payment, and he can boost income from off-farm employment. With partial-farm retirement, use of machinery and labor is less efficient and operators are pressed to buy or rent additional acreage to offset this, thus pushing another farmer out of the industry.

Land withdrawal also can be concentrated by regions of poorest soil or least comparative advantage. This concentration is almost impossible, or inconsistent with program objectives, where the attempt is to disperse land reduction over all farms in all regions. When land withdrawal is concentrated in regions of lowest crop yields and the whole farm can be withdrawn, the total costs of production control can be lowered. The reasons have already been explained. Regional concentration of withdrawn farms has an advantage of greater permanence. When whole-farm retirement is scattered over all regions, cessation of the program typically results in the withdrawn farms, scattered among farms that are still operating, moving right back into production. In contrast, when land withdrawal is concentrated by regions on a whole-farm basis, and the area becomes covered with grass and trees with fewer farmers present, there is less tendency to put land back under the plow. Analyses of the past programs show that the cost of output control might be reduced by about 15 percent where whole-farm withdrawal is concentrated in the least productive regions.

If society favors voluntary control, with gains to participating farmers through direct payments and higher prices, why does it not use the least-cost method? While the least-cost method may be satisfactory to farmers, problems of an equitable distribution of the costs of supply control still arise. Both participating and nonparticipating farmers are aided—the former through payments, and the latter through the higher prices that result from the reduced output by participating farmers. But although the farm income problem is solved, an income problem is transferred to local businessmen and others in the rural community who suffer reduced sales and income as families close up their farms and move away. Undoubtedly, this is the reason that whole-farm and regional land retirement programs, or even the free market, have been unpopular and the main reliance of voluntary supply control has been on the more expensive and dispersed partial retirement method. The Conservation Reserve programs of the 1950's are examples of policies that aided the farmer but hurt the nonfarm members of the community. In contrast, under the partial-retirement method dispersed over all regions most farmers continue to operate the remainder of their unit and do not leave the community.

The major task in policy is to find a collection of instruments or program elements that provide a reasonable approach to a positive-sum outcome for all relevant groups and a long-run solution to farm problems. Various groups oriented to the rural region, including Congressmen who do not want to see their districts eliminated, resist regional adjustments which cause land to be withdrawn in concentrated areas, because they imply a smaller population and reduced support for business and institutional sectors of the agricultural community.* Because the nonfarm population of agricultural regions is no less important than the farm population, we need compensation means that make long-run regional adjustments just as acceptable to the former as to farmers and landowners. Perhaps this is the most important single need or restraint to be overcome in devising programs that will provide long-run solutions to the problems of surplus capacity and technical advance in commercial agriculture.

Income sacrifices from rapid technological improvements have also been redressed through government storage programs. The CCC, initiated in 1933 to withdraw output from the market after it is already produced, still serves as a price supporting mechanism. Theoretically, a government storage program can serve to stabilize marketing and prices between years and seasons, thus reducing uncertainty and increasing the income of farmers. It also can be used as an indirect system of subsidizing farmers by means of income transfers or compensation. While the CCC has been used somewhat for both purposes, it has more nearly served in the second capacity over most of its life.

The CCC has used nonrecourse loans to remove grain from the market, thus causing prices to be higher at harvest, when supplies are large, and during years of large production. With surpluses arising every year, the CCC added to its stocks continuously in the 1950's. Without production control, there was no limit to growth of CCC-held stocks.

The mammoth accumulation of stocks by the CCC up to

---

* Perhaps a means to make Congressmen "as well or better off" after adjustment is to create a House of Lords made up only of those whose districts are eliminated by population shifts. It would be a self-liquidating house; while members would have life tenure, they would not be replaced.

1960 provided visible evidence—in the magnitudes of Treasury costs for storage and grain storage bins over the country—that something had to be done. Foreign disposal and large international food aids were initiated at that time. Grain and cotton were shipped to underdeveloped countries at no cost or for nonconvertible local currency, which the United States largely accumulates in the recipient country. This use of existing CCC stocks was not costly to the American public because it owned these stocks of food anyway. And since the costs of storing the mountain of stocks was so large, public expenditures could be reduced simply by shipping the commodities abroad at no return. Burning them would have been even cheaper but inconsistent with the values of the public.

Storage programs that allow the farmer to produce freely but that also withhold his product from the market (under nonrecourse loans or similar procedures), thus giving him a price above the market, represent an indirect form of price subsidy. This indirect subsidy is more costly than direct price subsidies because of the storage costs and facilities involved. If we are to avoid the accumulation of excessive stocks, we must eventually place stored commodities on the market at a lower price with the public making up the difference. Otherwise, outsize stocks accumulate, as during the 1950's, the carrying charges become staggering, and the subsidy program crumbles under the weight of its accumulated stocks. Price improvement through public acquisition of surpluses and dumping abroad, either as market food or donations, also is more costly than outright price subsidies. In the United States programs, the public paid the farmer for his product through CCC loans, paid for storing it for two or three years, and then gave it away. It always costs less to pay a farmer for not producing his crop; the payment only has to equal his normal profit. But if he is paid for it after he produces it, as during the 1950's, he must have the normal profit plus the production costs.

Use of public storage as a price supporting mechanism causes the CCC to serve as an indirect method of subsidizing or compensating farmers. Use of the facility for stability purposes alone would require a different orientation—one that is needed for commercial farmers in the long run. For stability purposes, the CCC would not accumulate stocks in order to raise prices. Its storage would be rather modest and represent the theoretical average amount by which yields in good years exceed those in poor years over an appropriate span of time. Because demand is inelastic, taking the surplus off the market in bumper years would support prices and increase farm income; the quantity would be put on the market in years of poor harvests to stabilize prices. This procedure would help to avert the instability and uncertainty of farming. Similar stabilizing mechanisms would be useful for hogs and other livestock where production swings in cycles, prices being disastrously low in some years and very high in other years when farmers have little to sell. These same stability mechanisms also can benefit the consumer by providing more stable flows of commodities and reducing fluctuations in retail prices.

Large carry-overs in grains and cotton developed in the 1950's because CCC storage was used mainly as a means of compensation—thus submerging its function as an instrument for stability. It should be converted to a pure stability mechanism. Storage for stability purposes will take on added importance if the nation gives even more food aid to underdeveloped countries. Disaster would indeed prevail if countries began to depend on us for food and then had to starve because we had a bad harvest and a small carry-over. Because of the vagaries of climate and the unique response of agricultural production to prices, stability mechanisms will be needed for agriculture even if we solve the problems of excess capacity and structural adjustments to a smaller labor force and larger farms are ultimately solved.

· · ·

The commercial farm policies that have been used in recent years have had broad economic, political, and social impact on the rural community. But the important question is whether these policy instruments have been efficient relative to the ends toward which they were directed, or whether more efficient ones are possible.

One of the many policy alternatives is reliance solely on the open market and the structure of pure competition, with their particular scatter of sacrifices and gains from technical advance and general progress in agriculture. Up to now, society has rejected this as a pure approach, through its investment in public schools, roads, police forces, and even production of new agricultural technology. It has done so by regulating food and drugs, by attempting to control the business cycle, and by providing unemployment compensation and social security.

In agriculture, as in other sectors, the basic functions of the price and market mechanisms need retention and strengthening, supplemented by public policy where (1) complete reliance on the market fails to provide the best achievement of national goals and (2) the distribution of gains and losses through the pricing mechanism are deemed by society to be inequitable and incompatible with guarantee of aggregate gain. Of course, the free market mechanism could have served to squeeze surplus resources out of agriculture, given sufficient time and widespread bankruptcy of farmers. But other methods can supplement the pricing mechanisms to salvage the dignity and capital values of individuals.

Some people argue vigorously that agriculture should be turned back entirely to pure competition of the free market with complete liquidation of all government policies. Others point out that agriculture is the only industry with a purely free market and that pure competition is not characteristic of the American economy.

Perhaps eventually domestic and foreign demand will

grow enough to allow agriculture to depend more fully on supply and demand conditions. But until that time arrives, a sudden return to free markets would force grave hardships on many farmers. Some would gain, but others would go bankrupt. Studies by Cornell University, Iowa State University, and the U.S. Department of Agriculture indicate that a return to a completely free market in the late 1950's would have caused prices to decline by 20 percent and, because of the high fixed costs of farming, farm income to be nearly halved—even with excess stocks of the time held completely off the market. Capital values would melt away and the assets of many families would be reduced. Hence, the problem of equity in the distribution of the outcome arises. The major problem of long-run solutions through the free market is the short-run incidence of sacrifices for different groups of farmers. While the immediate impact would be lower returns for most producers, the depression of income would fall heaviest in marginal areas. It would also fall heavily on the businesses that serve agriculture in marginal communities.

United States agriculture has never functioned in a completely free market. It is also true that the firms and households of few other sectors serve subserviently as price takers. Finally, government programs that have removed the intense price competition among farmers have *not removed competition from agriculture*. Of course, in the markets for labor, automobiles, television sets, and other services and commodities, short-run stability of price that allows the individual firm to retain some of the profits from progress has not eliminated competition in other directions. These other facets of competition, just as in nonfarm industries, cause the less efficient to be weeded out and still provide an overriding force toward progress in agriculture.

The higher and more stable prices under past farm policies themselves serve as an incentive for farmers to use more new capital resources and technologies. When the price of the product becomes fixed or stable, competition simply turns to the prices of labor and other resources employed in the output of the product. Land prices move upward and can be covered only by efficient farmers who use better technology; the inefficient ones can do better by giving up and moving to another occupation.

Past farm programs have not fallen short in restraining competition and progress in agriculture; rather, they have been more costly than necessary, have been extremely shortsighted and, in fact, have failed to solve the basic resource and structural problems of agriculture. Administered prices and managed supplies through public policy do not remove the factors that cause labor to back up in agriculture and take low returns. The problem of low farm incomes and resource returns, stemming from immobility of labor and other resources, is not likely to be solved by these policies. Administered prices have no long-run promise in eliminating the problem of low relative incomes of excess resources resulting from rapid technological progress.

The nation needs to turn more to consumer preference and the market mechanism as the basis for resource use and decision in agriculture. Even exports should be put more nearly on a commercial or market basis in the long run. More of the public subsidy needs to go into investments in people and not become dissipated simply in higher land values. However, the adjustment must be gradual and the size of the agricultural plant or supply needs to be shrunk to levels that are consistent with a greater play of prices, acceptable returns to farmers during the transition period, equitable treatment of nonfarm persons in rural communities that are faced with extreme adjustments through the pricing mechanism, foreign food commitments, and the inherent instability characteristics of agricultural production and prices. Certainly some mix of market prices and extra-market mechanisms will be required to meet these restraints and conditions. Supplementary to the market, long-run government policies are needed to provide price stability and an equitable distribution of the gains of agricultural progress.

The nation has invested enough in direct payments, price supports, and storage charges over the last thirty years to have solved the surplus problem several times over. Since the initiation of supply control policies in the 1930's, the nation has spent over $60 billion as direct payments to reduce output, as realized CCC commodity storage losses, as food shipments abroad, and by means of other direct and indirect price and production policies. This fund would have purchased nearly 840 million acres at national average land prices over the years of supply control programs. It would have purchased 300 million acres of cropland at $200 per acre. (Total cropland in the United States is about 500 million acres.) Quite obviously, surplus capacity could have been eliminated permanently at lower costs than the total outlay of the last thirty years, and it could have resulted in the shift of resources to more urgent national uses.

The temporary year-to-year programs, emphasizing the fractional withdrawal of land, can only postpone coming to face with reality. At the rate of current expenditures under short-run programs, we can spend $50 billion over the next ten years and still have the same problem with us. Furthermore, the costs of compensating agriculture through these short-run means has been increasing with the growth of agricultural technology and capital substitutes. This procedure perhaps was acceptable at the outset of surplus control programs, or even desirable as a short-run emergency measure during depression and postwar readjustments. It may have been justified at a time when we lacked sufficient knowledge of the extent and durability of the problem. But it can no longer be so justified.

The nation now needs a plan with a definite long-run objective underlying it and with a schedule of compensation payments for land diversion or other policy mechanisms that will actually solve the farm problem. Since the labor force and population of agriculture and rural towns are already declining, the plan should provide direction and assistance that will reduce problems of human adjustments. Permanent solution of the surplus capacity and structural problems require, among other things, large regional shifts in land use in line with relative advantage of different regions, the current size and distribution of the consuming population, and differential progress in farm technology over the nation.

A long-term program should provide for a gradual shift to more complete reliance on the pricing mechanism in resource allocation and allow diversion of some Treasury outlays to other public services and welfare needs that arise with a larger population, greater per capita income, and increased leisure time. Following the precedent of submarginal land purchases in the 1930's, the Conservation Reserve of the 1950's, and the Cropland Adjustment program of the 1960's, the nation should initiate steps to retire land over entire regions from crop production and convert it to recreation, grass, and other uses that are more urgently needed for a wealthy population. This shift should be large enough to curtail surplus potential and hold output to amounts that will maintain farm prices in the market at politically acceptable and economically equitable levels. Land in marginal producing areas would be retired permanently from field crops, according to comparative advantage, leaving the remainder of the nation's farmland in production. This would result in much larger and fewer farms in the adjusting regions, a trend that has been taking place rapidly even under the present programs.

The program should extend over a long enough period to limit the annual Treasury outlays required to attain its goals and the burden imposed on the nonfarm population in rural communities. The program cannot be accomplished too quickly, because of the tremendous income and adjustment burden imposed on the nonfarm population of the affected farm areas and the need to develop broader programs to aid and strengthen rural communities.

We must start from where we are, with cropland diversion scattered widely over all regions of the nation, and work gradually to a long-run adaptation of the agricultural plant consistent with domestic and foreign demand for food, through regional shifts in the use of land. The time period and the means involved should be economically acceptable to the rural communities faced with major adjustments. The following steps are directed toward this objective.

Adjusting regional use of land should be accomplished over a ten-year period. Starting from existing land diversion programs, the acreage shifted to other uses should be allowed to concentrate in marginal areas, on a regional basis, only at rates that do not exceed the ability of rural communities to absorb them or our ability to create programs to solve the problems and extend the economic opportunities of all people in rural communities. Simultaneously, controls on diverted land in other regions should be relaxed. Diversion of land would be on a whole-farm basis, thus resulting in subtraction of labor and capital, as well as land, from production of surplus crops. The market then should be used as the main means for allocating resources to different farm products. For foreign aid, the government should buy in the market those products desired by the recipient countries (rather than giving them surpluses representing a mix of products stemming from our historic price policies). The function of CCC should be turned to providing stability rather than compensation. Land should be withdrawn on a bid basis, thus guaranteeing that production control is on a least-cost basis and that only families who anticipate improvement would participate. One means of diversion would be direct land purchase by the federal government. However, other systems may have greater public acceptance for major land-use adjustments. The federal government might rent the land being diverted and then invest in seeding and other costs. An alternative with simpler administrative and managerial requirements would be purchase of farmer's rights to produce any crops but those specified. In this case, farmers would still handle the land, and most of the administrative and managerial problems in getting the shifts accomplished would fall into their hands. The payments, continued for a period of years, should have a specified termination date. Farmers then would be allowed to use the land for eligible purposes such as recreation, forestry, or grazing and payments would no longer be capitalized into land values. The rights could be turned back to farmers, perhaps at a price, should later growth in foreign and domestic demand so merit.

Reallocation of land from field crops to grazing, forestry, and recreation would require larger farm units in the adjusting regions. Similarly, the stocking of land and planting of trees would require additional investment by farmers and ranchers. Special credit facilities should be created to facilitate combinations of farms into units of profitable size and to span the period of diversion and development.

One major alternative has been outlined; others are possible. In any case, it would cost less to accomplish regional and structural adjustment of agriculture and to shrink the farm plant to levels consistent with current and prospective levels of demand than it would to continue existing programs indefinitely into the future. Furthermore, the basic problem can be solved in a definite number of years; otherwise the expenditure will continue and the problem will remain. Geared appropriately to the transition period, the overall program can fully compensate farmers in major adjusting regions and provide equitable treatment and opportunities for all people in rural communities.

The public must decide the level to which it will let farm

prices settle and, hence, the magnitude of the adjustment (that is, the total acreage shifted to other national uses). This decision may seem complex and loaded with value judgments, but the public is already making such judgments for agriculture as it invests in research and education to improve farming, irrigation, and conservation to increase output and as it invests in credit facilities to get more capital in use.

CHAPTER VIII

United States Agriculture and the World Food Crisis

In contrast to the United States, where food is abundant and cheap, many nations are plagued with food shortages. This problem, which has existed for centuries in many world regions, is acute in the less developed nations, especially those of Southeast Asia, Africa, and South America. The daily diet of half of the world's population is insufficient to allow normal physical efficiency. Their diets are as much as 100 grams of carbohydrates and a gram of protein per day below the minimum requirements for sustained physical activity. The table on page 154 indicates the wide variance in food consumption around the world.

Food deficits for backward countries are not in terms of the Western standard of dining, but only in providing for minimum biological needs. The entire daily intake of animal protein for one-half the people of the world is slightly less than that supplied in a single cup of milk. And these are

Daily Per Capita Food Intake by Major World Regions

| | ALL | | ANIMAL | |
REGION	CALORIES (NUMBER)	PROTEIN (GRAMS)	PROTEIN (GRAMS)	FAT (GRAMS)
Oceania	3,255	101	69	146
United States	3,190	95	64	146
Canada	3,110	96	64	140
Northwestern Europe	3,065	88	52	129
USSR	2,985	92	26	70
Eastern Europe	2,925	77	28	83
Mediterranean Europe	2,720	79	27	80
Latin America	2,570	66	23	60
Africa	2,455	64	11	44
Western Asia	2,370	74	13	40
China	2,200	65	6	32
Far East (excluding China)	2,120	55	9	32

averages. Many disadvantaged peoples have diets far under the average. The United Nation's Food and Agriculture Organization estimates that 500 million people suffer from active hunger and that 1 billion persons suffer malnutrition and diet deficiencies. Dire as these conditions are, the prospect will become even more bleak unless something is done to spur both food development and population control. Improvement in food production is not keeping up with the population growth in less developed countries. Some countries already are on the brink of subsistence and a single bad harvest throws them into disaster and starvation. Without surplus American wheat, as many as 10 million Indians would have starved to death as a result of the poor harvest in 1965.

But looming even greater is the mammoth growth in population projected for the future. Unfortunately, population growth rates tend to be highest in those countries of low income and food deficits. The rate of population growth has increased in the postwar period for two major reasons: (1)

improved medical and health services that prolong longevity, but especially save the lives of pregnant mothers and infants; (2) the larger population base from which births multiply. The eighteenth-century economist Thomas Malthus emphasized this tendency when he pointed out that population grows in a geometric ratio (1, 2, 4, 8, . . .) while food supply grows in an arithmetic ratio (1, 2, 3, 4, . . .). Hence, even a steady rate of population growth now adds many more people than the same growth rate did a century ago.

It is obvious, of course, that the world must face up to this fact and the implications for a pending food crisis. World population took 1,500 years to double, from the beginning of the Christian Era to 1600. It took three more centuries, from 1600 to 1900, to triple to 1.5 billion persons. But at current rates of increase, it will double again in thirty-five years; in Central and South America it will double in twenty-five years. Since this prospect prevails in a world where a major proportion of the population already suffers from malnutrition, this rate of growth cannot go unabated. Even if food could be supplied, standing space would eventually expire, a point that seems to escape those who argue that the solution to the world's pending food crisis is simply to increase food output.

While food production has moved ahead more rapidly than population and food demand in highly developed countries, the reverse has been true in underdeveloped countries. From early times to World War II, there was one general trade pattern: Western Europe was the importing region, and the rest of the world exported to it. Prior to the war, there were six grain-exporting areas: North America, 5 million tons; Latin America, 9 million tons; Eastern Europe, 5 million tons; and each of three other regions—Asia, Africa, and Oceania (New Zealand and Australia), small quantities. Western Europe has maintained its position as an importer—it buys about the same amount of grain as in the immediate prewar period to meet greater population needs.

Far-reaching changes have taken place in grain trade among other regions. Only North America and Oceania remain major exporters. Asia and Africa, on the other hand, have become net importers along with Latin America and Eastern Europe. Whereas less developed countries exported 11 million tons before the war, they now import about 24 million tons.

Not only has food production begun to lag behind population growth in the less developed nations, but also some more developed countries with large populations have recently stepped into the world market. With growing per capita incomes, increased consumer demand, and lagging agricultural development, Russia and other Eastern European countries have begun making sizable purchases of cereals from the United States. Canada has also contracted some large-scale sales with mainland China.

Given current rates of population growth, and without alternative solutions, the world's food situation will deteriorate materially in another fifteen years. Is this not the answer to the American farm problem? Should we not plow up the land idled under various programs, put it to crops, and ship the output to the countries with deficit diets and rapidly growing populations? Will not the mushrooming world population forever erase problems of oversupply in the United States and cause food to be in short quantity and high prices even here? Without a deep study of the situation, the answer to these questions would appear to be an unreserved Yes. In fact, many people urge that the nation immediately do away with its policies of supply management and price supports, and instead send the product abroad as gifts to alleviate hunger.

The answer to the world's population crisis is more complex than this, however. Even to produce surplus food and give it away over the world is not an easy task. As Colin Clark points out, the United States has persuaded India to accept more free food than any other country, but almost as a favor.* India does not want to live forever on donated food without developing her own food-producing capability. Wise economists and politicians, on both the sending and receiving end of food aid, should recognize these gifts as only temporary expediencies and move ahead to help the poor countries increase their own food output. Permanent dependence of one country on another for free food aid is undesirable and unrealistic.

People and societies abhor suffering through hunger and malnutrition, and all possible efficient steps should be taken to eliminate these problems on a worldwide basis. But it is possible to use policies that discourage development of food production and bring later misery to populations. It also is possible to dream of giving food to people who are in no position to receive it. A good number of the world's truly poor people live in remote areas where they eke out a living through subsistence farming. Not only are they used to their diets, but even if free food were made available they would have to carry it by baskets over long, winding paths. They will continue to do so until internal development brings them roads and storage facilities. Perhaps these should come before free food shipped from distant countries.

World growth in demand for food from the United States will not remove the nation's more basic economic problem: the structural adjustment of farming to economic growth and changed resource productivities and prices. Farms will continue to grow in size and specialization. Because there will be fewer of them and they will use less labor, the farm population will decline further and the rural community will suffer. These changes are likely to be intensified by any

---

* Colin Clark, *The Economics of Subsistence Agriculture* (New York: St. Martin's Press, 1966), p. 22.

demand improvement. They will even add to the nation's food-producing capacity.

The nation already uses world food needs as one means of lessening its stocks and utilizing its large farm-producing capacity. Food aid was largely responsible for reduction of public CCC stocks from 1.4 billion bushels in 1961 to .4 billion in 1967. With stocks stabilizing at about the required carry-over, an amount to meet fluctuations in yields between years and to provide pipe-line supplies for distribution, additional food aid will have to come out of annual production. Thus acreage restraints on wheat were already lifted for the 1967 crop.

Commercial exports have contributed similarly to demand. Before World War II, exports represented a minor use of the nation's farm output. The value of farm exports has increased by nearly fifteen times since 1940 and the physical volume has sextupled. Exports represent over one-half of total sales for wheat, rice, and soybeans, one-third for corn, sorghums, and cotton, and one-quarter for tobacco, barley, and animal fat. The bulk of these exports, two-thirds in recent years, have moved as commercial sales to the highly developed countries of Western Europe, Canada, and Japan. However, about 30 percent of total exports have gone under government assistance programs to other countries. This 30 percent perhaps should be regarded as purely surplus disposal, since the other 70 percent has moved under partial reflection of market demand and has returned some dollar currency that could be used for imports or other purposes in international markets. However, a total of 43 percent of farm exports has gone under some form of assistance —30 percent purely as aid without dollar return and 13 percent with government aid but some dollar return. Over 80 percent of the wheat exported moves under government programs, as does about one-third of the rice and cotton.

Of the farm surplus exported by the government, only

about 25 percent goes as outright aid. However, the remaining 75 percent nearly falls in this category since developing countries purchase it in their own currency. Under agreements for acceptance of the shipments, this currency is not convertible into the currencies of other countries so that it can be brought home. Neither can it be used to purchase commodities in the world market or the receiving country. It must be used within the receiving country for United States government purposes such as building embassies, or as gifts and loans to the country. Most of it goes for the second purpose. Hence, in fact, these food shipments become gifts. The humanitarianism and public conscience these gifts reflect causes most individuals and groups to favor them. International food aid seems to cause less controversy than other major domestic and international public programs.

There are several reasons why it has been hard for the United States to give away food. In the early years of food aid programs, American appropriations for these purposes were made only a year at a time. Since other countries could not tell whether Congress would appropriate funds for another year, they were reluctant to begin counting on this food and then have it discontinued. Further, since it came from accumulated United States surpluses, liquidation of these stocks through food donations also meant the end of the source. Other exporting countries such as Australia and Canada objected intensely to our giving away food, because American surpluses—mainly wheat, feed grains, and cotton —dumped into developing countries served indirectly as substitutes for their commercial exports and depressed world prices. Some developing countries could accept little free food because they lacked ports, storage facilities, and transportation to handle it.

In recent years, American food aid has become somewhat more permanent, and countries such as Pakistan and India have incorporated it into long-run planning. It has come in handy on a smaller scale to a good many countries and has been an emergency source to tide a few over the effects of severe droughts. But even these uses of surplus stocks for developing nations and disaster situations were not able to absorb the nation's excess producing capacity. While food has been exported as gifts and through other noncommercial or public shipments since the end of World War II, it cannot be given away as rapidly as American productive capacity grows. Even under international food aid programs, surplus stocks began to decline only after domestic production control programs were initiated on a sufficiently large scale in the 1960's.

Yet if population continues to grow at present rates, the world's population would double in the next thirty-five years and would press food needs hard against production potential. The world's land area cannot double; nor can food production easily do so. For the world as a whole, the problem is not whether there will be a food surplus, but whether the world can feed itself. The United States must fit into this picture and also be ready to supply growing exports to its usual commercial customers among the developed countries.

How this nation's food capacity may best help solve world population and food problems is not yet clear. The immediate problem is to coordinate our output with the growing demand for our food. Economists in the Department of Agriculture estimate that if all farmers did as well as the top 25 percent, we could double our output of food in 10 years; the rate at which farming ranks are being thinned will soon leave only this top 25 percent. It is hard to imagine that world demand for American food can increase at this pace. Over the longer run, the demand on our agriculture will be greater, but the best hope of the nation's agriculture is economic development, rather than a world population explosion that crushes people into misery.

A different approach seems more relevant for food needs relating to rapid population growth in underdeveloped countries. The United States alone does not have the resources to feed even one-third more people in the world. If it tried to do so, it would have to buy the food it ships as aid, once existing surplus stocks were depleted. Surplus capacity would then be eliminated, but the cost of the food shipments might be just as large as the current government costs of farm programs that pay farmers for not producing.

Extremely long-run population growth is only a remote problem in advanced countries. Knowledge and technology have been able to hold birthrates in check and to boost food output so that it exceeds population growth. And investments in capital processes and technical knowledge may give emergence to large food supplies from nonagricultural resources, such as the sea and chemical laboratories, before farm resources place a restraint on output and boost the real price of food within these countries.

The pressing short-run problem is in the less developed countries, the majority of which have only recently become independent and thus able to determine their own national policies. The balancing of growth in population and food supply is one of the major problems that most of them must solve in the next decade. The world crisis of population growth rates sharply exceeding food growth rates is perhaps three decades away. But for some individual countries the time is shorter.

Actually, the problem is not one of balance. Food output and consumption will be balanced in three decades even if there are ten times as many people subsisting on a miserable 1,900 calories per day. The basic problem more nearly is management of food supplies and populations so that they are balanced at levels that provide adequate diets and human welfare.

A society that invests first in steel mills and international airlines operated at a deficit, but lets population surge to press in extreme misery against food supply, can be considered as guilty as the dictator who shoots healthy people. Murdering well-fed people is really no worse than allowing masses of people to suffer and perhaps die from insufficient food and health facilities.

How do the agricultures of highly developed countries together fit into this picture? Cannot the abundance of food and the potential of greater output in these countries be channeled to the food-deficit countries, thus warding off the crisis and even helping to lift the level of human well-being? This would be a simple solution—if it were possible. And it would satisfy the humanitarian interests and intentions of the many individuals, groups, organizations, and nations. But it is unrealistic as the major answer to the world's pending food crisis and may mislead national or even world policies.

To be certain, the agricultural resources of the United States and other developed nations have an important and significant role in this complex of food and population. But the solution to the food problem lies elsewhere than in providing the increment of food required for an uncontrolled increase in the world's population over the next half century. If world population goes forward unchecked, untapped food-producing potential of both developed and undeveloped countries will soon be absorbed, thus ultimately causing even more starvation and misery. Ethical questions even arise as to whether societies should provide health and medical services that decrease mortality rates without parallel investments to increase food supply for the greater number of persons.

An almost equally complex question is that of international finance and trade to move food commodities among nations. Few societies can afford, or will consider it an obligation, to produce food and give it free of charge to countries who do not face up to questions of population increase. It is equally doubtful that developing countries wish their people fed forever in this uncertain manner.

To an extent, blind production increases in developed countries, to be converted to food handouts for less developed nations, even discourage the improvement of agriculture and growth of food supplies in less developed countries. Thrown into the market without price safeguards, they can lower the profitability of improvement by cultivators and farmers in countries where population is large and food production is small. In the last decade, food aid from the United States has diverted appropriate attention from the more fundamental long-run problems of birth control and population management in developing countries.

Food production should be developed in both the short run and long run where it is most economic and returns the greatest payoff on investment. In the short run, the payoff often will be greater in countries such as the United States with highly developed agriculture and underutilized capacity. This is true because of educational and organizational restraints involved in short-term adjustment of the agricultural structure in most less developed countries. But over the long run, the payoff is almost certain to be greater in improvement of agriculture in developing countries with favorable resource endowments and tardy technological developments. These countries are using resource inputs at such low levels that their marginal response should be much greater than in developed nations where resources are used nearer the optimum level. Of course, for some developed nations with a clear long-run comparative advantage in food production, and in some less developed countries with clear advantages in industry over agriculture, further developments should follow these lines, with trade catalyzed by appropriate international, commercial, fiscal, and investment policies.*

It is high time that proper priority be given to improvement of agriculture in developing countries where resources are favorable and populations are pressing. Too many countries, as history is beginning to reveal, have minimized agricultural investment in attempting to leap-frog into advanced industrialization. They must develop long-range plans and invest more in resources needed to provide an enlarged and economic supply of food.

But they must combine agricultural development with heavy investments in knowledge and technology of birth control. Population control represents the final long-run solution to the food problems of developing countries, but it will return much more on the investment than will agricultural development in bringing population into a realistic and humanitarian balance with future food supply.

Excess production capacity of the United States and other developed countries can be used effectively to meet short-run emergency problems in world food supplies. The payoff in the short-run from investment in more seed, fertilizer, tractors, and fuel for these purposes will be quicker and greater in developed countries where farmers already have the know-how and only need to have their abilities unleashed. The short-run return is much lower in countries where knowledge and experience lag ten or more years behind. The emphasis should be on stocks to meet weather emergencies and similar calamities, and on helping lift a few countries out of the squeeze they now find themselves in, with the remaining aid directed toward helping less developed countries help themselves. Food aid perhaps should be given only to countries that agree to invest appropriately

---

* See in this series, J. Pen, *A Primer on International Trade* (New York: Random House, 1967).

in both development of their own agriculture and in birth control.

Development of agriculture requires more human resources and is more difficult than developing a steel mill, building an international hotel, or instituting malaria control. That kind of development can be managed by a few government administrators and construction foremen. But improved farming must result from increased knowledge and incentive of millions of cultivators and peasants.

Here is where the United States can make its large and basic contribution to the world food problem—by furnishing the resources that help get development under way. These resources may include fertilizer, seeds, insecticides, or the plants and other resources to produce these inputs. In some cases they include investment funds. But most important are the intellectual resources of research, education, management, and organization that can identify and communicate knowledge of improved farming methods and introduce new technical capital in developing countries.

It is in this last category that the United States has excelled. It is hard to find another nation where public policy has been better designed to promote agricultural development. The United States increased the supply and lowered the prices of resources, at the same time bolstering commodity prices relative to input prices and sometimes subsidizing the cost of inputs. Both price forces encourage use of inputs, extension of output, and development of agriculture. These and related steps, including the provision of capital and the organization of a system to channel advanced technical knowledge to producers, are the effective economic elements of agricultural development anywhere in the world. It is this set of tools, if they can be effectively transplanted, that will serve most in aiding the development of agriculture in less developed countries. Part of this mix is necessarily that of management and organization ability to implement action programs and knowledge. *Organizational and manage-*

ment experience are perhaps even more scarce than capital as resources in most less developed countries.

These intellectual resources and economic conditions, rather than food, are the large long-run contributions that can be made from the experiences and capabilities of our agriculture. The nation has great resources, in its sixty-eight land grant universities and the U.S. Department of Agriculture, for making this fundamental contribution to world food production—and hence to improved economic development. We have growing opportunity to divert more of our public resources accordingly since private industry has begun to assume more of the responsibility of research and knowledge communication to our own agriculture. Furthermore, the halving of farm numbers and the farm work force should somewhat reduce the amount of public resources required to service the sector of commercial farmers.

Once we have solved our own problems of structural change and immobile resources that depress resource returns, we should be better able to help other nations transform their agriculture. Immobility of labor and depressed incomes are the rule of agriculture over the entire world.

As part of programs of the Agency for International Development (AID) and of other organizations, agricultural scientists and educational experts have been included in the "developmental package" sent to initiate and improve economic growth in the less developed countries. Their initial efforts were not always successful because they were inexperienced and did not have the proper organizations to support them. But the task has been accepted by the nation as a long-run effort, and experience of American agriculturalists with the cultures and traditions of less developed societies has now advanced greatly. The payoff from previous experience will show up in the future as this work continues.

We can also train more experts from abroad in our agricultural colleges and universities. Although many are being trained now, the number should be quadrupled if we are serious about helping the world meet its future food crises. Current training programs tend to revolve only around college-oriented youth, but not all advancement of agriculture in underdeveloped countries needs this degree of sophistication in knowledge. Some of the high school vocational agricultural departments that are closing down because of the declining number of American farmers could be used to train foreign youth.

Solution of the food and population problem over time goes even deeper. It rests on general economic development in the emerging countries. It is not reasonable to expect that burgeoning populations will forever be content to have their diets lifted slightly but continue to live generally at an extreme poverty level. While the race between food and population growth will continue as a basic world problem, we must set our sights higher. A public conscience has developed over the world that says economic development should progress to a level where the masses of people will have living standards that exceed subsistence diets.

The means of improvement and payment for imports must eventually be supported through internal economic growth. Not only is economic development the overall hope of less developed countries but it is also a means of promoting a more positive outlook for welfare of farmers in food-exporting nations. Much of the world's population has per capita incomes that average only $60 (India) to $300 (Mexico) per year. If population and growth rates are only at levels to keep diets and income at the subsistence level, the role of the United States and other developed countries will continue to be mainly that of giving food for humanitarian reasons. With sustained and more rapid economic development, however, world food demand is likely to expand greatly on a sound market basis. Food-deficit countries then can finance their larger food requirements from their own exports and increments in national income.

If per capita incomes were to quadruple among the poorer half of the world's population, the resulting income benefits to American farmers would be greater than those caused by any other combination of domestic and international forces. With slow economic development and a population expansion that keeps diets at the subsistence level, major exports to the less developed world will continue to be cereals such as wheat and rice But with sufficient economic growth and increases in per capita incomes, food demand increases for livestock products and the soybeans and feed grains required to produce them. Japan, a country that has enjoyed great economic growth in the postwar period, is an excellent example illustrating the effect of economic development on increasing the demand for our farm products. The elasticity of food demand with respect to income is high in the less developed countries. As per capita incomes grow, the increment of food demand increases by about equal proportions in some countries of large populations. The increase in demand for food imports grows in even greater proportions.

Domestic farm policies that provide a more realistic pricing of agricultural products can greatly aid the flow of our food exports into world commercial markets. Hence, American farmers might best rest their long-run hopes on realistic domestic policies and on more rapid and sustained economic growth of the less developed countries. This is a brighter prospect for the nation's farm prosperity than all of the technological improvements and population growth in sight.

Even if the best hopes were realized, with world economic development erasing all problems of surplus in the United States, the nation still would have the task of helping agriculture and the rural community adjust to the forces of domestic economic growth, and of investing in policies and facilities that provide economic opportunity for those released from farms and country towns as agriculture improves further.

Bibliography

History of Agricultural Policy

The three best historical summaries of long-run agricultural policies in the United States are: M. R. Benedict, *Farm Policies of the United States, 1790–1950* (New York: Twentieth Century Fund, 1953); Harold Halcrow, *Agricultural Policy of the United States* (New York: Prentice-Hall, 1953); A. Richard Spencer, *U.S. Agricultural Policy in the Postwar Years, 1954–1963* (Washington: Congressional Quarterly Series, 1963).

Fundamental Problems of Agriculture

Two books dealing particularly with the basic causes or variables of farm problems are the following: Earl O. Heady and Luther G. Tweeten, *Resource Demand and Structure of the Agricultural Industry* (Ames: Iowa State University Press, 1963); T. W. Schultz, *Production and Welfare of Agriculture* (New York: Macmillan, 1949); Lauren Soth, *The Embarrassment of Plenty* (New York: Thomas Y. Crowell, 1965).

Politics of Agriculture

Since agricultural policy has long been caught up in political conflict, the following books serve usefully in explaining the political environment of agriculture: Don F. Hadwiger and Ross B. Talbott, *Pressures and Protests—The Kennedy Farm Program and the Wheat Referendum of 1963* (San Francisco: Chandler Publishing Company, 1966); Dale Hathaway, *Government and Agriculture: Public Policy in a Democratic Society* (New York: Macmillan, 1964); Reo M. Christenson, *The Brannan Plan: Farm Politics and Policy* (Ann Arbor: University of Michigan Press, 1959); C. M. McFadyen, *The Farm Bureau and the New Deal* (Urbana: University of Illinois Press, 1961).

Basic Analysis of Agricultural Policy

Several books that analyze agricultural policy and program needs are: Earl O. Heady, *Agricultural Policy Under Economic Development* (Ames: Iowa State University Press, 1962); M. R. Benedict, *Can We Solve the Farm Problem?* (New York: Twentieth Century Fund, 1956); Willard W. Cochrane, *Farm Prices, Myth or Reality* (Minneapolis: University of Minnesota Press, 1958); Center for Agricultural and Economic Development, *Problems and Policies of American Agriculture* (Ames: Iowa State University Press, 1959); Earl O. Heady *et al.* (eds.), *Agricultural Adjustment Problems in a Growing Economy* (Ames: Iowa State University Press, 1958).

World Food and Development Problems

Books evaluating the food situation and agricultural development problems of the world include: Center for Agricultural and Economic Development, *The Economic Development of Agriculture* (Ames: Iowa State University Press, 1965); R. F. Mikesell, *Agricultural Surplus and Foreign Policy* (Washington: American Enterprise Association, 1958); T. W. Schultz, *Transforming Traditional Agriculture* (New Haven: Yale University Press, 1964); Center for Agricultural and Economic Development, *Food: One Tool in International Development* (Ames: Iowa State University Press, 1963).

Index

A NOTE ON THE TYPE

This book was set on the Linotype in BASKERVILLE, *a facsimile of the type designed by John Baskerville, Birmingham, England, in 1754. The original Baskerville type was one of the forerunners of the "modern" style of type faces. The Linotype copy was cut under the supervision of George W. Jones of London.*

Design by Leon Bolognese